Tales of
NORMANSFIELD
The Langdon Down Legacy

ANDY MERRIMAN

The DSA is a Registered Charity
that relies almost entirely on voluntary donations

First published by the Down's Syndrome Association 2007

Down's Syndrome Association
Langdon Down Centre,
2A Langdon Park
Teddington
Middlesex
TW11 9PS
United Kingdom

Tel: 0845 230-0372

www.dsa-uk.com

ISBN 978 0 9555228 0 2

Designed & produced for the DSA by Phil Bushell. Tel: 020 8889 9744

Printed & bound in Great Britain by William Clowes Ltd, Beccles, Suffolk

ACKNOWLEDGMENTS

Tales of Normansfield: The Langdon Down Legacy is very much a team effort and I would like to thank some of the key players . . . in fact, the numbers now constitute a rather large squad . . .

There are two people in particular without whom this book would never have been written. Firstly; a very special thank you to Heather Cadbury, who not only worked at Normansfield but has dedicated huge amounts of her time to research, interviews and articles about the institution. I am totally indebted to Heather for her help, encouragement and support.

Many thanks to Professor Conor Ward for his advice and assistance, his work at the Langdon Down Trust and for the definitive biography of John Langdon Down from which I have borrowed shamelessly . . .

I am also grateful to Sandra Maltby and Rosalind Chislett at the Langdon Down Charitable Trust for their guidance.

A special mention must go, of course to the ex-residents of Normansfield and their relatives who have entrusted me with their unique stories, particularly David Towell, Anthony Shillingford, Miles Holroyd, Jessica Merrilees, Brian and Elspet Rix, Bev Purnell, and Brian Ware. Also to ex staff members of staff including, Wolfgang Stange, Carol Rentoul and Miriam Bruinsma.

The following also afforded me interviews, time and material; Steve Curran, (Kingston Primary Care Trust) Michelle Whitmore, Joan Bicknell, Denise Carr, John Dunkley (Tamesis Rowing Club) Jane Taylor, Director, 'Owl Housing', Rosalind Georgeson, (Dragon Drama) and Lindsay Walton.

I am indebted to Peter Longman, John Earl (The Theatres Trust) and Francesca Byrne for their knowledge and contributions in regard to the Normansfield theatre. Thanks also to staff at the London Metropolitan Archive, 'ace' researcher, Jess Campbell, 'cub' reporter Daniel Merriman and my wife, Allie, for her constant support.

A special thanks to all the staff of the Down's Syndrome Association, especially Carol Boys, Paul Zanon Ellie Walsh and, of course, the information and research section: Susannah Seyman, Stuart Mills and Ruth Beckmann. Their knowledge is unparalleled and their enthusiasm boundless.

Finally thanks to my brilliant editor, Rick Glanvill, and equally clever designer, Phil Bushell.

PICTURE ACKNOWLEDGMENTS: I am very grateful to the Langdon Down Charitable Trust for permission to reproduce photographs, letters and illustrations from their archive, which constitutes most of the illustrative material. My warmest thanks also go to photographers: Michelle Whitmore (p.13); Miriam Bruinsma (p. 100, 158, 186 & 195); Fiona Field (p. 148, 247 & 248); Denise Carr (p. 240); Daniel Merriman (p. 256). My courtesy for additional images goes to: the Theatres Trust (p. 88 & 96); Miles Holroyd for the Una Dunville watercolour painted by her aunt, Bertha Lambart (p.169); Wolfgang Stange for the photograph of Gordon Bairnsfather (p. 208), the oil portrait by George Beven (p. 212) and the photographs on pages 222-223. The photograph of the statue 'Girl with Hoop' (p. 252) was taken by the sculptor, Andre Wallace.

Every effort has been made to contact all contributors and copyright holders of material reproduced in this book. If any have been inadvertently overlooked, please accept our apologies.

An un-named patient in the early days of Normansfield, 'Mongolian idiot' or dignified gentleman?

CONTENTS

PREFACE

'The patients are sixteen in number. Upon our visit today we found them assembled in two parties at tea. They were well dressed, cheerful and happy in aspect and apparently in good bodily health. The accommodation arrangements generally are on a very superior order and the staff of attendants and nurses is ample. A brougham and wagonette [horse-drawn carriages] are available for drives.

With three exceptions the patients walk daily beyond the grounds which comprise about five acres, and will when aid and planted afford abundant means for exercise and recreation… the patients were at their meal with their attendants and the several masters and mistresses who have charge of them.

Great attention is evidently given to the neatness and cleanliness of both sexes and the conduct of all was orderly … what we saw of the diet was very good: beef, rabbits, apple pudding and corn flour with wine, beer, milk or water according to the direction of Dr Down.'

**Lunacy Commissioners,
reports on visits to Normansfield, 1868 and 1895**

'I was the first to arrive from my group and was immediately hit by the smell that was a mixture of lino, boiled cabbage, disinfectant and urine. When the rest of my party arrived a male nurse took us for a tour of the hospital. Our first stop was upstairs in the old building and along a long corridor with rooms off it.

This, we were told, was the challenging behaviour wing. Many of the people who 'challenged' were naked. A woman was lying on the floor of the corridor blocking our path. We were not at all sure of what to do but the nurse told us to just step over her. It felt so awkward; I had never had to step over a naked person before. We asked why people were naked and were told, "Well, they ruin their clothes when they wear them."

Our next stop was a building in the grounds, which housed thirty or forty men, many of whom rushed to greet us as we entered, thrilled to be visited. I soon became aware that the ceiling was covered in stuffed animals, which were taped to the ceiling. It was the most bizarre sight. The explanation was that they had been given to the patients but as they would be likely to damage or destroy them, the toys were taped to the ceiling so that the patients could look at them without touching.

All of the men slept in a room with their beds about three feet apart. Each bed had a locker next to it, standard National Health Service issue, and was separated by a square of net curtain. This net curtain did not run to the floor or the whole length of the bed. This, we were told, was to give the men some privacy. How, I do not know.

A door was opened to show us one of the bathrooms. A man was in the bath and tried desperately to cover himself from the seven or so strangers. Not once did the nurse address him or apologise for the intrusion. We were appalled and embarrassed and just wanted to get the hell out of there and leave the man to have his bath.

There was a woman being pulled about the corridor with her nightgown up around her ears. The general noise levels were deafening. There was a sense of being in a kind of underworld where rules and expectations were a million miles away from what was acceptable at the time. An aura of secrecy about what the staff were up to... and that we shouldn't really see what was going on. It was Hogarthian. I really have never forgotten that visit and how awful the whole experience was.'

Susannah Seyman,
Information Officer, Down's Syndrome Association
report on visit to Normansfield, 1983

CHAPTER ONE

A SUITABLE CASE

Oh, Mary, this London's a wonderful sight
With people here working by day and by night
They don't sow potatoes, nor barley nor wheat
But there' gangs of them digging for gold in the streets
At least when I asked them that's what I was told
So I just took a hand at this diggin' for gold
But for all that I found there I might as well be
Where the Mountains of Mourne sweep down to the sea.

'The Mountains Of Mourne'
William Percy French (1854-1920)

It is late February 1997. A tiny, blind, silver-haired woman almost as old as the century and bent double by her arched spine rests momentarily on the arm of a carer. The elderly lady's escort whispers words of encouragement to her charge and they begin to trudge along the corridor of a shabby Victorian hospital. After 71 years at Normansfield, a hospital for the learning disabled, Patricia Collen is being discharged. She is going home.

Patricia spent most of her long life in Normansfield. We are fortunate that her time there was recorded with such diligence for the hospital's archives. Her singular experience represents that of so many.

Since Pat's admission in 1926, there has been one world war and many more conflicts. The British Empire has ceased to exist, silent movies have become talkies, the cathode ray has held universal sway, several British monarchs have come and gone, a man has walked on the moon for the first time and virtual reality is no longer a technological miracle. During all these epoch-making events Patricia, because of her physical disabilities and 'a mild mental handicap of an unknown origin', has spent most of her life institutionalised. The only event that has radically improved her life was the move from a hospital ward, where her few possessions were stored in a standard issue locker, to a room of her own - and even then only a few years before her discharge.

Patricia Finlayson Collen was born in Oxford in 1916. Her mother, Constance, died of pneumonia at the age of 38 when Patricia was just eighteen months old. According to Normansfield's medical notes, on admission, 'Mother was never strong, very anaemic and nervous. She lost two children through stillbirths.' It is possible that Constance may have had German measles when pregnant with Patricia.

Patricia's father Richard, who owned a linen mill in County Armagh, was described as 'a gentle, mild mannered man, ten or more years younger than his wife.' Richard's own father, John, Patricia's grandfather, was a wealthy builder who raised his family in the opulent surroundings of the Killycomaine House Castle in Portadown. Constance had also came from a moneyed background. Her sister, Kate, had two children of her own but was apparently not in a position to take in Patricia when Constance passed away.

In 1926, Patricia was referred by her father to see a Dr A F Tredgold who wrote: 'She does not know the days of the week, is unable to do simple addition or subtraction, has difficulty in understanding, does not dress or undress herself, requires supervision. In the past, wakeful and screamed, feeds herself, occasionally wet at night. Backward speaking, pokes fingers in her eyes, no concentration. Eyes defective, no convulsions, nurse left after three months.'

Interestingly, this same Dr Tredgold had authored a book in 1911 entitled *Mental Deficiency* in which he claimed: 'There exist persons of inferior intelligence whom we may term dullards. The dullards are followed by the class designated as "feeble minded"; the feeble minded merge imperceptibly into the imbeciles and these again are connected by insensible gradations with the idiots. The gross idiot is characterised by a complete negation of intellect and thus stands at the lowest extreme of mental development.'

And in a later edition of the book he concluded: 'Many of the defectives are utterly helpless, repulsive and revolting in manners.

The elegant Patricia Collen in her own home . . . finally.

Richard and Constance Collen's household.

Their existence is a perpetual source of sorrow and unhappiness to their parents. In my opinion it would be an economical and humane procedure were their very existence to be painlessly terminated.'

In view of Dr Tredgold's rather jaundiced views, it was hardly surprising that following the consultation of June 1926, Richard Collen wrote to Dr Reginald Langdon Down, son of Normansfield's founder, John Langdon Down, thus:

> *28th June 1926*
>
> *Holly Brook, Gerrards Cross, Bucks,*
>
> *Dear sir,*
>
> *My only child a girl of 10 years is a strong healthy well made girl, but mentally frail, she has average vision but does not use her eyes.*
>
> *Kindly give me particulars of your place.*
>
> *Yours faithfully,*
> *Richard Collen*

Reginald Langdon Down wasted no time in replying the following day:

> Dear sir,
>
> In reply to your letter 28th inst I am sending you a paper giving terms and other particulars of this home, and shall be happy to make an appointment for you to come and see our arrangements if you wish.
>
> Yours faithfully

The following week, Richard Collen responded:

> 8/7/26
>
> Dear Dr Down,
>
> I do not like the word imbecile so I return the form you might let me have others with feeble minded on.
>
> Yours faithfully,
> Richard Collen

Once again Reginald's response was swift:

> 9th July 1926
>
> Dear Mr Collen,
>
> In accordance with your request I am sending you the forms which should be used if your little girl is to be certified as a 'feeble minded' person, filled in as far as I am in a position to do so. I need not send a fresh statement of particulars for you if you will kindly initial the alteration in the description I have made.
>
> The extract from the Act giving definition:
>
> . . . feeble minded persons; that is to say, persons in whose case there exists from birth or from an early age mental defects not amounting to imbecility, yet so pronounced that they require care, supervision and control for their own protection or for the protection of others, or in the case of children that they by reason of such defectiveness appear to be permanently incapable of receiving proper benefit from the instruction in ordinary schools.

After a few days consideration, Richard Collen's reply was somewhat perfunctory:

> *14/7/26*
>
> *Dr Down,*
>
> *I am now returning forms completed. I am arranging to have Patricia ready and I will take to reside at your place on Monday 26th July, please say what time of day, morning is more convenient. When sending a/c make it to the end of Oct, future 1/4ly a/cs (quarterly accounts) can commence on 1st Mon. I expect she will be the 150 Guineas arrangement.*

This cursory missive describing his daughter as 'the 150 Guineas arrangement' (presumably relating to her level of care) determined Patricia's future life, and at the age of ten she was consigned to a lifetime's institutional care at Normansfield. Richard Collen obviously believed it was the best thing he could do for his 'feeble minded' daughter and the brevity of the letter may have been his way of coping with the heartbreak that he surely must have felt.

He had looked after her for nearly a decade and even with the support of maids, housekeepers and servants, he must have been convinced that Patricia was better off in full-time care.

It is interesting that even in 1926 Richard Collen was concerned about the terminology used to describe his daughter. For the last couple of centuries people with what we now call learning difficulties have been the subject of many terms.

Lunatics, congenital idiots, feeble minded, imbeciles, dullards, mental deficients, moral defectives, mentally handicapped, subnormals (this as late as the 1970's) have been some of the words used by doctors and other professionals over the years. These are not insults – they are professional terms and the result of various legislations over the last few 100 years.

It is comforting to know that Richard Collen did not just dump his daughter at Normansfield or relinquish all responsibility, but visited regularly and corresponded routinely until his death in 1953.

Letters from Mrs Langdon Down kept Richard fully informed about his daughter:

January 1926

You have seen her so recently that there is little I can add to what you already know. I am glad to tell you her health continues well and she is improving in self control and is as a rule well behaved. She is still learning new tunes and new words to the tunes, but she does not make much progress at school. She is under treatment of the dentist.

24th February 1926

Not quite the thing. Bed and cold, slight cough.

Richard Collen also provided an extensive wardrobe for his daughter and the clothes were always purchased from Harrods. A list from 1927 included: 'a velveteen winter coat, navy serge dresses, one cheap panama hat, brown walking shoes, bronze sandals and rational corsets.'

Reginald Langdon Down, like his father before him, was a keen photographer and in April 1927, he wrote to Richard Collen, 'Patricia photographed last week and I am sending you the proofs herewith. Let me know which. Price one dozen. 6x4. 27/-.'

By today's prices these are the equivalent of over £50, but what's a proud parent to do? And no doubt they were of superior quality to somewhere like the local 'happy snap' shop.

In 1928, there followed a series of letters between the Langdon Downs and Richard Collen in regard to Patricia's health. With each communication there was also a request for Richard to Collen to settle his daughter's account for her residency at Normansfield:

2nd April 1928

a/c due

Patricia out of sorts on and off last day or two. Yesterday her face was rather blotchy and today erupted in spots . . . being in bed opportunity to examine her and whether effectively vaccinated – no marks been vaccinated and whether you approve of me doing so.

Mrs L-D

I was so glad to hear this morning P is now well again. It is a great thing the weather is better and she was able to go out yesterday for a little. Give her my love.

Richard Collen

11th April 1928

Comfort to hear the eruption on Patricia's face is healing . . . did get a shock seeing her last Saturday.

Richard Collen

5th May 1928

Well behaved, quiet at night. Spots nearly healed.

6th June 1928

Face rather swollen again – bed and treatment.

Patricia had, of course, contracted measles, but by the end of the month she had recovered and was out of quarantine. For the next few years, she was troubled by various ailments and seemed particularly susceptible to skin complaints. The hospital staff kept Richard Collen up-to-date with the state of her health:

11th February 1930

I am glad to report that she is in good general health and is quiet and well behaved just now. She is still somewhat sore under the arm in the neighbourhood of where the boil was, as you know she is rather slow in healing.

5th November 1930

I am glad to be able to give you a good account about her on the whole with the exception of last week. I had her in bed for a day or two because she appeared to be faint and pale and she had a slight raise in temperature for a couple of days. Her indisposition however has now passed off.

Her father heard that Patricia enjoyed the firework display that took place on 5th November each year in the hospital's spacious grounds. She also spent several weeks in Worthing, where the hospital rented a school and a large number of patients and staff holidayed each summer:

5th August 1931

Good health when she left here with party for Worthing on Thursday and I have had good reports from (Matron) Miss Cheek there as to the health and happiness of her party there.

However, problems in regard to Patricia's raiment persisted:

Mr C

I return Patricia's a/c which is quite correct. We are ordering another pair of pyjamas as P has torn up her old ones, which leaves her with only three new pairs.

The following note also appears on Harrods headed paper:

12th December 1931

Miss L-D, dear madam

With reference to your telephone message we very much regret we are unable to obtain the evening dress selected by Miss P Collen in pink or blue size 38" before Christmas owing to it being made in Ireland. We are however venturing to forward a pink dress size 40 on approval as this could probably be altered. We have only a white size 38.

After Richard Collen passed away in 1953, Patricia enjoyed no further contact with family members for 40 years. Still, Patricia's progress in the intervening years was documented by a Normansfield psychiatrist 33 years on in April 1986:

Over the years, under a carefully planned and structured programme, she maintained her limited vocabulary and indeed learnt some nursery rhymes. She always participated in social and recreational activities. Additional handicap (registered blind), along with severe mental handicap, considerably hindered her achievements. She learnt how to enjoy the sound of birds, perfume of flowers and coach rides. Miss Collen always maintained good physical health. Her general condition is remarkably good for her age.

Miss Collen's activities are planned and implemented by hospital staff who care for her. Her daily activities are attending music and pottery classes and hydrotherapy. She is a pleasant lady who talks very little and will not be able to make any conversation. Her verbal communication is limited. She cannot dress, undress, or bath herself and needs help with feeding and in maintaining personal hygiene. Her memory is poor, she cannot recall any events of her childhood or any part of her life in hospital. She is not orientated to place, person and time. She loses direction and would not be able to direct herself back to the ward.

As she has reached the age of 70, one can expect a gradual fall in her skills. Indeed she may have already been showing some signs and symptoms of brain failure.

On examination I found that Miss Collen's ability to understand and her recollection of property is poor.

Two years previously, Patricia had been provided with the support of an independent advocate. Isobel Butler, who was employed as an administrator at the Royal Opera House, visited Pat regularly at Normansfield. Her bulletins on Pat's personality offer great insight:

Pat knows and comprehends much more than is at first obvious. She is, as far as I can tell totally blind although the other day she remarked that someone was wearing a blue dress! Her hands are deformed and she has difficulty in holding things.

Patricia thoroughly enjoyed going to Isobel's home to have Sunday lunch with Isobel and her mother. Not surprisingly, Pat's appetite was much more voracious during these visits than at Normansfield. According to Isobel, Pat had two helpings of the Sunday roast, while in the hospital she had to be persuaded to eat. Isobel also took Pat away on holidays and described her as very adaptable:

> *She likes to stay in hotels, although she can be a little difficult in*
> *that she wakes up at night and can be a bit noisy.*

Isobel reported that Patricia liked going out in the car and sang
along with any music that was on the car radio.

> *Her memory for music, especially hymns, Gilbert & Sullivan and*
> *music hall music, is good. One of the nurses used to take her to church*
> *on Sunday mornings and she thoroughly enjoyed a good sing.*

Isobel commented that Patricia was often much more cheerful and
communicative the more she visited. She described Pat as having a
great sense of humour and quite a giggler! Other times Isobel
found Patricia to be quite withdrawn, which she put down to a
desire for more individual attention and stimulation.

Isobel provided a statement in support of Patricia's needs which
she ended by saying:

> *I feel that a move to a smaller unit which would provide her with*
> *this sort of attention would do her good. Pat's surroundings at*
> *Normansfield are very pleasant although there are some people*
> *who are far more handicapped living in the same bungalow.*
> *She is extremely well looked after. She is happy as far as I can*
> *tell. She is always clean and tidy.*

With the proposed closure of the hospital in the mid 1980's, an official
solicitor was appointed and the following is a statement made to the
Court Protection by a Mrs S L Faulkner on 12th April 1990.

> *On 15th February I went to Normansfield to see Patricia and spoke*
> *to (Sycamore House manager) Pat Fernandez. I was introduced to*
> *Patricia as she was finishing her lunch. She is very small and needed*
> *a great deal of encouragement and assistance with eating her food*
> *as she has deformed hands. She is also totally blind now and so is*
> *obviously unable to eat without a certain amount of mess. She also*
> *needed encouragement to drink her orange juice. She was then helped*
> *from the dining room into the lounge where she sat in her own chair*
> *which has a little foot stool. She has some difficulty in walking but*
> *is able to get about with assistance. When she was introduced to me*

by my Christian name she repeated it and said, 'Hello.' Her response to any of the questions that I asked her was, 'I want to go out.'

She couldn't remember any of her family members.

I was told by staff that Miss Collen loves to go out, but that they are faced by a lack of transport. Car rides, as often as possible, would improve her quality of life no end. She is quite capable of appreciating a car ride to go out to tea, to have her hair done, or even go to the theatre or musical or a short trip to a restaurant. She loves having attention and being spoken to. She loves singing and music. She does appreciate flowers very much indeed and she and three other patients club together to buy a bunch of flowers every week. If they could afford agency staff they could take her out.

Patricia would also appreciate a wheelchair. This is not because she really needs one all the time but because it would give her more access to the outside world. She finds moving difficult and it is very slow and labour intensive. If she were to have a wheelchair she could be taken outside easily and would not need a worker or nurse with her the whole time.

Patricia also needs many more clothes. She was dressed in a pink blouse and Crimpoline jersey and a tweed skirt that had seen better days. The problems of washing were explained to me. There are eleven patients all of whom need frequent changes of clothes. Although the bungalow has an ordinary washing machine this cannot cope with the amount of washing and so some of it is sent out to a laundry. This not only takes a long time but also increases the chances of the clothes being mislaid.

I was taken to see Patricia's bedroom which she shares with one other patient. She has a tiny wardrobe with not many clothes in it and a tiny chest of drawers. She has a music centre but hardly any records (a possibility of buying her a compact disc system?). It would be most helpful if she could have a duvet, but this would need to be a very expensive one as it must be fire resistant.

Patricia does not readily respond to social advances made by the other patients. She just does not answer their questions. She will talk to the nurses and the carers, however. She has no friends as such. She has moods of being very withdrawn but can be very jolly especially on Wednesday evenings when a volunteer comes to play the organ and everybody sings. She has a good memory for nursery rhymes and old Irish songs and hymns.

Occasionally it is quite obvious that she has been brought by a caring family and will say things like, 'I will be a good girl today.' She has excellent manners. She loves having one to one attention and being talked to.

I then spoke to Vi Williams head of Accounts at Normansfield. She had had no approach from the nursing staff for further funds to be spent on such things and so no further action had been taken. She has no problem in obtaining money from the Public Trust Office and Patricia has £1000 a year pocket money which is spent on clothes and holidays. She did think that Patricia would appreciate a second holiday. The problems of staffing a second week's holiday is that a member of staff has to give up a week of their own holiday and is only paid £100 for this. The intricacies of clothes purchase and the monitoring of laundry were explained to me as were the numerous forms that have to be completed for the release of any money for the benefit of the patients.

It is extremely frustrating to think that Patricia actually had access to monies which would have made a significant difference to her quality of life but yet which she did not see because of staffing or bureaucratic complexities.

Fortunately for Pat, it was during this time that a relative, Anthony Shillingford, was traced by the official solicitor. Neither Anthony nor any of his family knew of Patricia's existence until then, at which stage he became Patricia's official receiver. When Anthony began visiting Patricia, he found her to be very shy and retiring and somewhat overwhelmed by other noisier and more demanding patients.

And so plans for Pat's discharge were initiated. A series of meetings with Owl Housing Ltd, an organisation providing support services for people with learning disabilities, determined Pat's needs for living independently. It was fortuitous that Pat's contact at Owl Housing, and current Director, Jane Taylor, had previously worked at Normansfield. She had left to work in other areas of learning disability before setting up Owl Housing in the reprovision programme. 'We catered specifically for Patricia's physical needs and didn't concentrate on her learning disability,' Jane recalls. 'She didn't have any behavioural problems and was, in fact, quite undemanding. She simply required practical support.'

A carer and a housekeeper were thus employed from family funds.

Pat was indeed extremely fortunate to be financially secure and from the family estate, Owl Housing, with help from the public trustees office, acquired a house near Normansfield for Pat and two other hospital residents to live. These three women were actually the last patients to leave Normansfield on 27th February 1997. Within two years, one of the women had died and the other was transferred to a nursing home. After 73 years, Patricia finally had a home of her own!

Patricia was immediately comfortable in her new environment, sleeping and eating well, and she started to enjoy the use of her new garden. Within several months, under the guidance of her Care Manager, Patricia was attending the Avenue Day Centre for music sessions, having regular hairdressing appointments and making regular shopping trips to Kingston upon Thames. There were also visits to other houses to meet up with former residents with whom Patricia had spent her years at Normansfield.

Since 2004, Patricia has been looked after by carers Michelle and husband George and with their care and devotion has made great progress. Although blind, mainly confined to a wheelchair and needing help with most aspects of personal care, Patricia leads an active life as possible. On a recent visit an aromatherapist, who has been treating Patricia for a year, had just finished a consultation. Judging by the evidence of 'before and after' photographs, the therapy has certainly made a difference to Pat's health and appearance. Patricia was very elegantly attired in cashmere sweater and corduroy trousers. It wasn't clear whether she is still purchasing her clothes from Harrods of Knightsbridge, but you would not be surprised.

Patricia loves going on outings and still adores listening to music. She is extremely popular and according to one of her carers, 'inspires affection'. She likes to play the piano and still knows the words to 'Danny Boy'. According to Anthony Shillingford:

> . . . the extent of her activities has now been tailored to suit her moods and enthusiasms and she has become the centre of attention. Compared to the shy lady at Normansfield, she is now much more open and communicative and is now able to share laughter and music with children and adults in the neighbourhood.

Pat is a regular churchgoer and extraordinarily, at the age of 89, exercised her rights as a citizen for the first time to vote in the 2005 General Election. Michelle provided her with the necessary information about the three main parties and on the basis of this, Patricia made her own choice.

Patricia is taken out every day and often has lunch at her favourite French bistro. She loves visiting Hampton Court and National Trust properties and always attends pantomime performance at the Richmond Theatre. She has had regular holidays and in 2007, there are plans for her to return to Ireland to visit her ancestral home.

It has taken a very long time – literally a lifetime – for Patricia to live some kind of independent life and she is finally receiving the care and attention that she needed many years ago. Who knows what she may have achieved in her lifetime, given the opportunities that some children with learning and physical disabilities are now given? Despite the fact that Patricia's family were extremely well heeled, she was denied the possibility of a life fulfilled.

Patricia Collen was one of the last patients to leave Normansfield and typifies the residents who occupied the hospital for most of the 129 years that the Langdon Down dynasty and then the NHS ran the renowned institution. Hers is a quintessential tale of the treatment of someone who was just a little bit different . . . there are many others.

CHAPTER TWO

IMBECILES, IDIOTS & THE FEEBLE MINDED

Instead of my understanding being addressed and enlightened, and my path being made as clear and plain as possible, in consideration of my confusion, I was . . . placed amongst strangers, without introduction, explanation or exhortation.

'A Narrative of the Treatment Experienced by a Gentleman, During a State of Mental Derangement' John Perceval (1840)

I t is possible that without a chance meeting in 1846, John Langdon Down might not have become involved in what was to become a lifetime's work and the birth of a family dynasty that ran the hospital for nearly a hundred years. According to a report in *The Medical Times*:

Taking refuge from inclement weather in a country inn, John Langdon Down came across a girl – 'a semi-idiotic woman of feeble mind' – who was waiting on the party. Some years later, he described his feelings about her: 'A question haunted me – could nothing for her be done? I had then not entered on a medical student's career, but ever and anon the remembrance of that hapless girl presented itself to me and I longed to do something for her kind.'

I too am drawn to the predicament of that 'hapless girl' but for a much more personal reason. For this waitress was probably not much older than my own daughter, Sarah, who has Down's syndrome. And it was her dramatic birth some fifteen years ago that thrust me, somewhat reluctantly, into the world of disability and 'difference'.

The treatment of imbeciles, idiots and the feeble minded throughout history has been one of distrust, fear and segregation. In their book, *The Politics of Mental Handicap*, Joanna Ryan and Frank Thomas suggest:

> *Institutionalising people is the way society deals with people it finds useless, dangerous or inconvenient.*

Sarah is certainly not useless or dangerous but although like most children she might dispute the fact, her presence is occasionally inconvenient. It is Sarah who is my muse as I write this account because, had she born in a different era, she could easily have been a patient at such an institution as Normansfield.

These institutions, which multiplied without restraint during the Victorian era, were constructed in countryside or outlying suburbs and always outside populated areas. The men, women and children whose lives were affected by physical or mental disability or a mental illness needed to be hidden away. They were different, and therefore dangerous. It wasn't so much them who needed to be in a safe place and protected from themselves, it was mainstream society that had to be shielded from these 'deviants.'

As Steve Humphries and Pamela Gordon write in their book, *Out Of Sight*:

> *The best way of curbing numbers of the disabled was to segregate them. Disabled people represented as helpless, threatening or insane were thought to be one of the main causes of poverty, unemployment, criminality, alcoholism and idleness.*

And within these institutions, men and women were separated as there was the belief that learning disabled people were highly promiscuous – moral degenerates.

Although this book chronicles the specific history of Normansfield and is therefore not the place to document detailed legislation, it is important to give some historical perspective.

Workhouses, first established in the 1630's, were common in most market towns by the middle of the 18th century and became

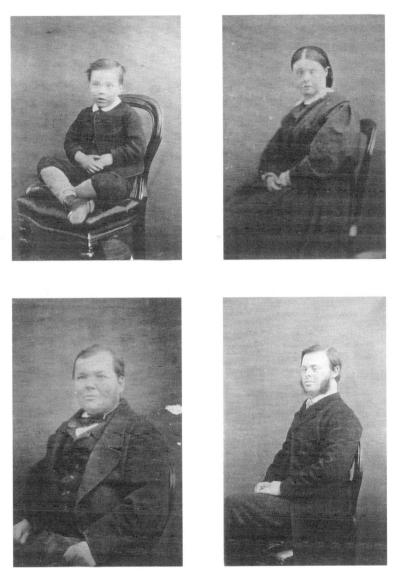

Four Earlswood patients of the 1860's.

the dumping grounds for 'the decrepit and dependent' of all descriptions. Following The Poor Law Amendment Act of 1834, local parishes combined forces with others and, as Unions, established one large workhouse for each area governed by a Board of Guardians.

The 1845 County Asylums Act compelled every county and borough in England and Wales to provide asylum treatment for all its 'pauper lunatics' and in the same year the Lunacy Act established the Lunacy Commission. Its principle functions were to monitor the erection of a network of publicly owned county asylums, the transfer of all pauper lunatics from workhouses and outdoor relief to a public or private asylum and to regulate their treatment in private asylums.

The Lunacy Commission was also empowered to regulate the county asylums and to monitor the admission and discharge of patients in hospitals for the insane. The Commission consisted of three doctors, three barristers, and up to five unpaid lay commissioners. A more detailed form of certification was devised, which supposedly increased the safeguards against wrongful detention for both pauper and private patients.

In 1840, Andrew Reed, a philanthropist, expressed a hope that he might be allowed to do something for:

> . . . Fellow creatures who were separate and alone but with the Divine image stamped upon all.

After a public meeting at the London Tavern, Bishopsgate Street, in October 1847, it was resolved to proceed with a project to establish the first asylum for idiots in Britain.

As Humphries and Gordon wrote:

> The following year, Park House, Highgate had been acquired and 54 boys and 12 girls were admitted for training. As the demand for beds increased, some residents from Park House were later moved into Essex Hall, Colchester, and also the newly built 'model asylum' at Earlswood in Redhill, Surrey – a charitable institution which sought to aid the 'respectable poor' of Victorian Britain. Earlswood opened in 1852 and within three years, there were three hundred adults and children in residence.

John Langdon Down, who had been studying medicine at the London Hospital Medical School, was a protégé of a Dr William J Little, who was also consulting physician to Earlswood. Under

John Langdon Down.

Little's patronage, John Langdon Down was put in charge of the Earlswood Asylum in 1858 – undoubtedly the best-known institution for 'idiots and imbeciles' for much of the nineteenth and twentieth century.

Langdon Down was still qualifying as a doctor and actually had no experience in institutional treatment, let alone the treatment and education of 'idiot' children. His training had in fact been as a pharmacist, working under the supervision of his father in Cornwall, before moving to London and then finding work as a chemist, reportedly assisting the pioneer scientist Michael Faraday in some of his now famous experiments.

John Langdon Down extolled the virtues of separate institutional care and education of 'idiot children'. He emphasised the lack of scientific education available to such children in pauper institutions and advocated idiot institutions separate from lunatic asylums. By the late 1860's Langdon Down and his young assistant, George Shuttleworth, were responsible for supervising the treatment of 600 inmates in Earlswood.

Langdon Down was medical superintendent of the Asylum between 1858 and 1868 and it was during this period that he developed his own 'moral treatment of idiots' – an educational system based on an arrangement of rewards and punishments and a practice that he was to take with him to Normansfield.

According to David Wright, author of *Mental Disability in Victorian England*, 'corporal punishment was strictly prohibited but there were more subtle means of punishment and persuasion within the confines of everyday life.' Privileges such as access to sports and trips were utilised as a means of reinforcing appropriate behaviour. Langdon Down believed, 'the idiot has to learn obedience, that doing right is productive of pleasure and that wrong is followed by deprivation thereof.'

The selection and admission procedure to institutions such as Earlswood is interesting. The huge demand in accommodation for idiots and lunatics in the 19th century was driven by families of all social and geographical backgrounds, seeking institutional care for their children. Prior to the opening of specialised institutions the 'feeble-minded' were either kept at home or, when relatives could no longer cope, sent to the poor house or the asylum for the mentally ill.

Initially, the family sought application for a place, usually endorsed by respectable member of community – vicar, medical practitioner or magistrate. In the case of 'idiot children' reception orders were signed jointly by a local clergyman, doctor or magistrate and a guardian (invariably the father)

Earlswood placed a limit on the number of private patients it would admit in any given year. It was after all a charity asylum built for the poorer classes with only a few beds for private patients. As a consequence, there were numbers of wealthy families willing to pay significant sums to have 'an idiot child' looked after in the institution.

Children were educated as far as possible and then trained in a variety of trades such as carpentry, brush-making, printing, shoe-making, tailoring, laundry and domestic work and work in farm and garden. Order and routine was established in their lives, daily exercise and leisure pursuits encouraged. The Victorian period witnessed a dramatic change in the education of the mentally disabled. Prior to the 19th century, the ineducability of idiots had been a common belief.

Institutions such as Earlswood represented a radical experiment in education and were based on a post enlightenment belief in the 'perfectibility of humankind', a Victorian faith in self-improvement. The structure of the asylum undermined one of its fundamental purposes, namely to teach idiots and imbecile children domestic and vocational skills and return them to their communities and family environments. Residents at Earlswood were seen as pupils and patients, highlighting Langdon Down's belief in the use of education and training alongside medical treatment. Physical recreation including cricket and football and music played an important part in the lives of Earlswood residents.

One of John Langdon Down's most celebrated patients at Earlswood was the extraordinary James Henry Pullen. Pullen was born into an artisan family from Dalston in 1835 and was one of thirteen children, most of whom died in childhood.

Pullen was originally admitted to Essex Hall and then transferred to Earlswood in 1850. He only started to talk at the age of seven – apparently only managing to articulate the word 'muvver' for a long time. He was profoundly deaf and thus never went to school, although he learned to spell and write names of simple objects. He had an extraordinary talent for numbers

'The Admiral'.
With the patronage of the
Prince of Wales one of Langdon
Down's most celebrated patients
was the extraordinary James
Henry Pullen. He was
admitted to Earlswood in 1850
at the age of 15. He was put to
work in the carpenter's shop,
rapidly becoming an expert
craftsman producing all sorts of
furniture as well as a 'fleet' of
model ships. Pullen has been
cited as one of the most
celebrated 'Idiots Savants'.

As a child he began to carve small ships out of firewood and then draw pictures of them. At Earlswood, he was put to work in the carpenter's shop, rapidly becoming an expert craftsman producing chairs, bookcases and all sorts of furniture. He even built beds for the hospital wards. An exceptional example of his work is the model of the steamship 'Great Eastern' – Brunel's famous paddle steamer – which took him more than three years to complete. Pullen completed every part himself, down to the brass anchors and copper paddles. He also crafted a representation of the 'Princess Alexandra', a six-foot long, 40-gun man o'war. The model of this took pride of place in the asylum at every public occasion and was exhibited in London and Paris, where it won a bronze medal. Queen Victoria owned some of his drawings and he had the patronage of the Prince of Wales, who sent pieces of ivory for carving. Pullen referred to him as 'Friend Wales'. Pullen made a huge number of small carvings in wood and ivory, which he sold for pocket money in pubs around Redhill.

On one occasion he returned to the asylum very much the worse for drink and got a severe reprimand from a Dr Caldecott. He later signed the Pledge and never drank again.

There are varying reports about his behaviour. Some suggest he was 'quiet, well behaved, good tempered and generally perfectly happy'. Others describe him as 'reserved and sullen, stubborn, intolerant of supervision, suspicious of strangers and easily affronted by busybodies'.

It does appear that Pullen was quick to anger if his requests were not granted. He took a dislike to one of the Earlswood staff members and spent much time planning a grisly death for this particular man. Pullen erected a 'diabolical guillotine' over one of the doors in the hospital. Apparently the contraption went off a fraction too late and the steward was saved. The hospital's case book also notes that, 'On one occasion he (Pullen) threatened to blow up the place because a request had been refused, and it is quite likely that he would have attempted to do so had he not been mollified. On another occasion he did partially wreck his workshop in a fit of passion'.

Visitors came from all over the world to see his work and with all this adulation, he became very conceited. Another note in the case book describes him as 'the quintessence of self conceit' and the ubiquitous Dr A F Tredgold noted that while showing him his handiwork, Pullen would frequently tap his own head and say, 'Very clever'.

On one of his expeditions outside the hospital grounds, Pullen met a young woman, fell in love and insisted that he be discharged from Earlswood so that he could marry her. He was refused permission - it appears that he was quite a draw at the hospital and something of a money-spinner for the institution. Lovelorn and moping, Pullen refused to do any work or communicate.

Eventually, Pullen was summoned by one of the Governors to the board room and was told that he could leave if he wanted but that they would be sorry to lose him and that if he would reconsider, they would grant him a commission in the Royal Navy as an Admiral of the Fleet. A dazzling naval uniform of blue and gold resplendent with brass buttons was procured and shown to Pullen. He became more smitten with the uniform than his intended bride, who was never mentioned again. 'Admiral' James Henry Pullen donned the uniform on high days and holidays and ceremonial occasions.

Pullen has been cited as one of the most celebrated 'Idiots Savants'. Diana Cortazzi, a psychologist at Royal Earlswood who started the Museum in the 1960's, has made a special study of

Pullen and concluded that he was suffering from 'aphasia with high frequency deafness'.

He was indeed a remarkable man, whose powers of observation, detail and memory contrast with a childish simplicity. He was deprived of his freedom at a young age and although he attempted at times to free himself from the shackles of institutionalisation, he remained at the hospital until he died in 1916, aged 81. So famous had he become that his obituary appeared in *The Daily Telegraph*. (Interestingly, Pullen was not the only 'celebrity' patient at Earlswood. In 1941 the Queen Mother's two 'mentally handicapped' nieces, Katherine and Nerissa Bowes Lyon, were admitted to the hospital.)

According to Professor Conor Ward, the acclaimed biographer of John Langdon Down, 'The establishment at Earlswood had developed an international reputation and John Langdon Down had steered the asylum from crisis to crisis.' However, in December 1867, the Earlswood board was alerted to the fact that patients were being kept in the local community and suspected that Langdon Down was taking payments in addition to his contract. In fact, wives of two of the staff had started to house private patients in their cottages, and their husbands had received increased remuneration for their jobs as attendants at Earlswood.

Langdon Down admitted this was the case but claimed the whole arrangement was supervised by Mary Langdon Down. According to Conor Ward, 'Mary Langdon Down threw herself into the organisation of activities and entertainments for the residents, frequently performing many of the duties herself. She became involved in training programmes and in due course extended her work to include the supervision of residents who boarded with staff members and in other houses, but who had not been formally admitted to Earlswood. This was an additional source of income but was to be a bone of contention with the Governors at a later stage.'

Mary Langdon Down had actually played a central role in the smooth operation of Earlswood – counselling mothers, discussing problems with the matron and preparing social events, 'The Langdon Downs went outside the limits of the Earlswood system and without prior approval of the Board, set up an outreach programme. A number of patients were placed in the homes of

John's loyal wife,
Mary Langdon Down.
An awesome administrator
and driving force at
Normansfield, where she
became known by staff
and patients alike as
'Little Mother'.

staff members and other local families, to be supervised by Mary Langdon Down, who was not a hospital employee.'

The Board arranged a special meeting but before it could take place, Langdon Down tendered his resignation in February 1868. He had never formally requested remuneration for Mary and his actions were thus technically illegal. Apart from obvious embarrassment and wishing to avoid unwanted publicity, there may have been other reasons for his pre-emptive resignation.

David Wright, in *Mental Disability in Victorian England*, observed that:

> *The private trade in lunacy in madhouses persisted throughout*
> *the Victorian period – many medical superintendents, having spent*
> *years in pauper or charitable institutions gathering experience and*
> *cultivating connections with potential patients, left the public*
> *institutions for lucrative private practice.*

Langdon Down was no exception and, by now, the need for hospital places from wealthy clients was such that he also realised he could profit as proprietor of a private institution of his own. Shortly after his resignation he took up a Harley Street private practice and wrote a letter to his contacts, setting out his plan to secure premises and grounds near Wimbledon and to open a similar institution for 'payment cases'. He asked them to mention his plans 'to any persons having afflicted children to whom the information may be useful'.

Instead of moving to Wimbledon, Langdon Down received a licence to run a private establishment at the 'White House', Hampton Wick, near Teddington, Surrey. It would be called Normansfield.

CHAPTER THREE

A FRUITFUL OUTCOME

*An idiot is someone who knows nothing, can do
nothing, wants nothing and each idiot approaches
more or less to this point of incapacity.*

**Edouard Séguin (1846)
19th century advocate of special education**

nce purchased, 'The White House' (a family home which had been built two years earlier in 1865 but never occupied) was renamed 'Normansfield' in recognition of the Langdon Downs' solicitor, Norman Wilkinson, who helped the couple with mortgage arrangements. Normansfield was registered in the name of Mary Langdon Down and John Langdon Down assumed the title of Medical Superintendent. New wings were added to the original house and a recreational entertainment hall was built. The pair developed the five acres attached to the house and over the next 20 years acquired more properties and land together with the river field running down to the Thames, altogether totalling over 40 acres.

The Langdon Down family itself had been expanding: Everleigh, John and Mary's first son, had been born in 1861. A second son, Reginald, was also born in Earlswood in 1866 and their youngest son, Percival, was born within two weeks of moving into Normansfield. Their only daughter, Lilian, who died tragically at the age of two, had been born in 1865.

The hospital opened in May 1868 as a private home for the:

> . . . care, education and treatment of those of good social position
> who present any degree of mental deficiency.

Langdon Down felt strongly that children from these classes were somewhat deprived in such provision and that very little was done for them. Normansfield was to supply a need for a residential training and care for the learning disabled of the upper classes.

The Normansfield residents varied in age from toddlers to adults and there were almost as twice as many boys as girls. Not all the residents had learning difficulties – some experienced various physical disabilities, such as blindness and cerebral palsy. Between the years of 1868 and 1896, nearly 60 patients suffered from epilepsy and were treated with bromide with some success.

Some admissions were as a result of the death of one parent, usually the mother, but in rare cases the death of both parents. According to Conor Ward:

> A Chief Justice in the British Legal System in India had two sons in Normansfield, some residents came from Europe and one child whose parents were Moroccan spoke only Arabic.

OCCUPATION OF FATHERS: 1868-1893

Landowners	16
Army/Navy Officers	15
Lawyers	14
Gentlemen	24
Merchants	29
Doctors	5
Civil Servants	18
Clergy	18
Not entered	87

In the first year, nineteen residents were admitted (by the time John Langdon Down died in 1896 there were 160) and each pupil, according to his or her ability, was taught 'life skills' such as dressing, feeding and cooking, the use of money, weights and measures and buying and selling.

Interestingly, John Langdon Down's vision and philosophy of care for Normansfield are set out in *Quain's Dictionary of Medicine*, published in 1882:

> *The patient should be rescued from his solitary life and have the companionship of his peers. He should be surrounded by influences both of art and nature, calculated to make his life joyous, to arouse his observation, and to quicken his power of thought . . . success can only be obtained by keeping the patient in the highest possible health. Diet should be liberal . . . moral education is of paramount importance. He has to learn obedience; that right-doing is productive of pleasure and that wrong-doing is followed by the deprivation thereof . . . he should be taught to dress and undress himself, to acquire habits of order and neatness, to use the spoon or knife and fork, to walk with . . . the defective speech is best overcome by a well arranged plan of tongue gymnastics followed by a cultivation of the purely imitative powers.'*

Activities at Normansfield demonstrated Langdon Down's beliefs: teachers were engaged and artisan workshops were developed where young people could be instructed in crafts. Initially staff

The 'Artisan' workshops with head carpenter, James Bradley, in the foreground.

41

were recruited from the immediate vicinity and several local families provided the mainstay of support. The record of long service at Normansfield contains the names of people from all departments in the hospital, including nurses, domestics, artisans, farmhands and gardeners.

Instruction was given in dancing, gymnastics, music and languages and an elegant entertainment hall was built which was also used for Sunday services. Amongst other activities, there was riding, cycling, cricket, tennis and football. There were also Punch and Judy performances, donkey cart rides and every year over 100 residents visited Crystal Palace.

Mary Langdon Down's immaculate bookkeeping notes detail seaside excursions, piano tuning, and music library membership. On Sundays those who were able attended Sunday Service in the theatre and the men and the boys were given flowers to wear in their buttonholes.

The land was actively farmed, with a herd of white pigs known as 'Normansfield Large Whites'. Cows and chickens and a productive garden provided food for the kitchens and occupation for the patients. Entertainment had to be provided and employment agencies were used for the recruitment of staff that could sing, act or play a musical instrument. A lower floor, the kindersaal, was a huge playroom for the younger children.

Langdon Down's intention was that Normansfield should be run on the principles of a family home, accommodating an extended family. On 27th December 1869, the Commissioners in Lunacy reported that all the available residents dined together on Christmas Day along with the attendants and nurses and some of the younger members of the Langdon Down family were also in attendance. Every resident received a personal Christmas gift from John and Mary Langdon Down. Conor Ward comments:

> *Whereas in Earlswood the residents slept in large dormitories, in Normansfield they were in groups of three or four. The girls were under the care of a governess and six nurses. The ordinary pattern of care was for a group of residents to share a large room and to have a staff member to sleep with them, constituting a pattern of continuity, aimed at giving the residents a new sense of family. A single staff member was responsible for each group of patients.*

A veritable menagerie in the hospital grounds.

"That's the way to do it." Punch & Judy visit Normansfield.

This attempt to provide a family atmosphere within the institution was paramount in the Langdon Downs' philosophy of care, reflecting their own feelings on the strength of family life and it would prove instrumental in the institution's success.

In the schoolroom children learned reading, writing and arithmetic. Written progress reports were sent to their parents. When the Commissioners visited on 22nd October 1879 they found the boys to be:

> . . . *of orderly demeanour and taking great interest in their school work.*

One of the pupils to attend these lessons a little later was George Fryham Haffenden. Born in Ealing in 1881, he was described as suffering from 'epilepsy and imbecility'. His mother, Frances Madeira Haffenden, was a copious letter writer and his father, also George, was a civil servant and a Justice of the Peace.

Below is one of George's examination results at the turn of the 20th century:

Report from Trematon. Result of Christmas Examination 1899

Name: G F Haffenden

Subjects	Position Obtained
Behaviour	G
Geography	F
History	G
Dictation	writing improving
English Grammar	F
Arithmetic	F
Shorthand	-
Euclid	-
Algebra	F
French	F
Latin	-
Drawing	-
Drill/physical	F

Signed: N Halloway, Headmaster

George Haffenden was obviously not strong enough in either Euclid or Latin to be tested, but it is interesting to note that both subjects were in the Normansfield curriculum. The Haffendens' younger son attended Marlborough school where, no doubt, he would have achieved excellent grades in both Euclid and Latin.

The family travelled extensively in Europe and seem to have led a very full life. However, Mrs Haffenden by no means neglected 'Fry' (as she called her son) and there is much correspondence about his epilepsy, dental work and his wish to grow a beard! Mrs Haffenden is also not backward at coming forward when it comes to the fees:

> *Whilst most willing that Fry should have the advantage of a visit to the sea side, I cannot but think that the cost per head is rather heavy and the period for these visits has increased. Originally they were for a fortnight – then for an optimal fortnight or three weeks, but now it is for a fixed month. If I have an option I should say for three weeks at a consequently reduced cost.*

George Haffenden remained at Normansfield for the rest of his life and was described in the casebooks as mainly well behaved, but occasionally mischievous ('takes laces out of others' boots'). He worked in the garden and learned the trade of French polishing, but presumably remained a stranger to the geometric genius of Greek mathematicians. Him and me together.

The first patient ever to be admitted to Normansfield was the 21 year old William 'C', who had cerebral palsy, reportedly caused by the effects of sunstroke during a journey from India via the Suez canal. William 'C' remained at Normansfield for 20 years until he died of pneumonia. He had actually been a patient at Earlswood – one of the many who followed John Langdon Down to Normansfield. Indeed, the significant number of private patients who had previously appeared on Earlswood registers and were then admitted to Normansfield would seem to confirm the fact that his move in the mid-1860's was pre-meditated.

Mary Arnott was the third patient to be admitted to Normansfield and she was actually the first with Down's syndrome. Mary had also been one of the patients who had been living with a staff member at Earlswood under Mary Langdon Down's supervision.

Arnott was born in Marlow, Buckinghamshire, in 1850 and was just eighteen when she was transferred to Normansfield on 12th May 1868. The Registry of Admissions states that Mary suffered from 'imbecility' and was 'a congenital idiot'. In *Casebook 1* she is further described as having:

> *Lymphatic temperament, course skin, lips furrowed and a large*
> *tongue with enlarged papilla. Her circulation is feeble and she is*
> *liable to chill blains. She menstruates regularly. Her other bodily*
> *functions are normal. She is an imbecile in mind. She talks very*
> *much but with little understanding. She is extremely obstinate,*
> *will not walk beyond the grounds and this obstinacy is most marked*
> *just antecedent to menstruation. She can write a letter and play*
> *sometimes from memory on the piano. She is affectionate . . . and*
> *when free from ill temper is witty and cheerful. She nurses a doll*
> *which she calls "the baby" and this baby is the one to whom all*
> *bad qualities are conferred. Her mental peculiarities have existed*
> *from birth. Her father is healthy and of normal mental health.*
> *Her mother is highly nervous, delicate, physically and mentally.*
> *She can partially dress herself, and partly take care of her person.*
> *She is not epileptic. She has a slight tendency to lateral curvature of*
> *the spine and she stoops very much. She has converging strabismus*
> *and her voice is remarkably harsh.*

It's fascinating to think that Mary Arnott could play the piano and that even all those years ago it was felt that music could play a significant part in her life. Presumably this inspiration came from Mary's mother, who must have devoted much time, energy and love in caring for her daughter before feeling she could cope no more. Arnott's 'highly nervous' mother was actually a widow. Elizabeth Arnott lived at The Glade, Englefield Green, Egham, Surrey. There is much correspondence from Elizabeth Arnott to Mary Langdon Down. On occasion these letters are written by a servant, Adelaide Pearce, who tended to record complaints under Elizabeth Arnott's instruction. A letter dated December 1884 from Adelaide Pearce revealed, 'Mrs Arnott is anxious about Mary of whom she has heard nothing since more than a month and will feel obliged if you will let her know how her daughter is.'

Further letters make demands for better care for her daughter

Above:
Mary Arnott pictured
in her teenage years and
later as a well established
Normansfield resident,
until her death in 1907.

Left:
A missive from Mary
to Normansfield staff,
describing herself as
'a little lady'.

and Mrs Arnott, via Adelaide, wishes to ensure that Mary gets enough fresh air as she believes this will improve her health. In one letter Mrs Arnott writes that she is concerned about Mary's 'continued confinement to bed'. She comments that she would like Mary to have a walk in the garden chair each afternoon and a walk in the grounds in the morning.

Mary made relatively frequent visits home that varied in duration. There is one report of a three-week stay and there is a letter written by Mary Arnott while at home. The content is hard to make out and it is written in faint pencil (see photo on page 47). Over the next few years, according to the casebooks, Mary, 'continues in good health but remains obstinate'. By 1873, she enjoyed good health and 'improved general demeanour'.

It seems that due to her ill health, Mrs Arnott seldom visited her daughter at Normansfield but Mary continued to enjoy home visits to The Glade until her mother's death in 1886.

Mary herself died on 14th April 1907 from 'heart failure and senile decay'.

In a short space of time Normansfield attracted considerable public attention. In October 1877, fewer than ten years after Normansfield had opened, the Christian Union published an article describing the hospital:

> *In the pleasant country between Twickenham and Hampton Wick, an institution has been growing steadily for nine years which would probably rank among the most honourable, beneficial and fruitful outcomes of medical skill and philanthropy in England. That the Institution for the Feeble Minded at Normansfield should have been the work of one man, a consulting physician in the West End of London, rendered the success it has attained and the progress it is making all the more remarkable.*
>
> *With these convictions the writer purposes to record a recent visit to Normansfield . . . The boys and young men are domiciled in one wing of the buildings and the girls and children of either sex in another.*
>
> *Everything done is of direct utility to the object of the institution. The sheep, the horses, the fowls, the gay plumaged birds, the agreeable variety of busy, orderly labour going on about the place, are all of the same piece as the cricket field, and the rare flowers and plants with which the lawns and the walks are adorned. They*

contribute to the health and happiness of the inmates, and form a part of the education by which the light of intellect is made to shine over their hitherto benumbed and beclouded senses.

The training process of Dr Down has its foundation in the corpore sano. Good health of the patients remains the first consideration; this end secured, the means of which in diet, regimen, cleanliness of person and clothing and the most skilful medical supervision are so minute and complete as seldom to fail, the mental training proceeds in an easy, natural and patient progress from what is simple to what is more compound, till in the repeated individual exercise, and the helping and stimulating companionship an example of others, the feeble faculties begin to operate, and will and action to respond to each other with more or less steady force . . . Music has obviously the happiest effect on all this class of sufferers, of whatever age, or whatever degree of impotence not absolute.

It is no little alleviation of their case that when they are alive to the harmony and inspiration of sweet sounds. One sees then almost ecstatic pleasure beaming in the countenances of the whole group, younger and older, when singing together with their teacher, and accompanist on the piano. But to account for the strength that music gives to the understanding, it seems that a group, thus singing together, bring into concentrative play the sense of mutual support and strength which forms a vital element of the general system at Normansfield. Each feels that he or she has contributed to a powerful result and in this experience finds a basis of new individual effort.

Of the mental education under Dr Down and the masters and governesses it may be said that, while adapting to the ages and various degrees of ability of the pupils, and to carry upward to considerable results, it is wholly free from the formality and rigour of the schools . . . The efficacy of the law of kindness has seldom been more strikingly illustrated that in this Institution for the feeble mind. First perfect discipline is maintained without personal chastisement or material deprivation of any kind. No pupil is allowed to be shaken, or slapped, or deprived of necessary food, or subjected to any avengement.

The duty laid on teachers and attendants is to gain the affection of their wards so fully that nothing will be to them a higher punishment than the disapprobation, or negative withdrawal of the love of their ministrants.

The Institution at Normansfield is necessarily reserved for the *feeble and backward of the more wealthy classes, but the fact only suggests the question why the advantage of similar treatment should not be extended to the helpless offspring of the lower and more numerous ranks of society . . . Should not every county almost have an institution for imbeciles? Is there not a new question here for the state and for our legislators?'*

In 1867, Down gave an address to the Social Science Congress in which he made a case for the development of 'special services' for the learning disabled of all classes. Perhaps to assuage his conscience, he acted as consultant and fundraiser to a local provident dispensary – in effect a medical insurance club – and according to Conor Ward, Dr Down's continuing work at The London Hospital was unpaid.

Even so, he was hardly struggling financially. Normansfield was an institution almost exclusively for the learning disabled of the upper classes, who could afford private care for their relatives. The annual fees for each resident depended on the level of need, but averaged around £200 per year in the 1870's. Needless to say, this was not cheap. Normansfield was a real money spinner. Supplemented by his Harley Street practice, John Langdon Down and his family consequently made a vast fortune. In fact, in 1900, the estate was quoted at £48,656 – the equivalent of over £3.5 million in today's money.

John Langdon Down hosting the British Medical Association's visit to Normansfield in 1895.

CHAPTER FOUR

GOOD MAN ... QUIET MAN ... NOT QUITE MARRIED MAN

Why bustle thus about your door,
What means this bustle, Betty Foy?
Why are you in this mighty fret?
And why on horseback have you set
Him whom you love, your Idiot Boy?

She kisses o'er and o'er again
Him whom she loves, her Idiot Boy;
She's happy here, she's happy there,
She is uneasy every where;
Her limbs are all alive with joy

Extracts from 'The Idiot Boy'
William Wordsworth (1798)

In 2003, a year before the Down's Syndrome Association transferred their headquarters into the main block at Normansfield, Carol Boys, the Association's Chief Executive, visited the site of the hospital for the first time and recalls an almost mystical experience:

My husband Paul and I went into the old 'White House' where
the family first moved when they came to Teddington. It was cold,
dark and full of old rubbish left by the NHS after their sudden
departure. I wandered into the old dining room, the shutters were
closed and the room was very dark. Paul said, "You must look at
the fireplace in here, it's magnificent."

I moved to open the shutters to get a better look at the fireplace. There in the corner was a pile of rubbish, old curtains, cardboard boxes and old dishevelled files. As I leaned forward to open the shutter, the pile fell to the ground. Somehow, a small, battered suitcase mysteriously fell open and the contents seemed to fly through the air. As I picked up some of the objects, I discovered that they were a treasury of Victorian letters and keepsakes of one Walter Ridpath. I took the case outside and we read all the letters, some were to Dr Langdon Down, Mrs Langdon Down and others were obviously to staff and family. What a find! One or two were dated 1865, there was even a programme from a Christmas performance in the Theatre. Underneath the letters were a few photographs of young people with Down's syndrome in Victorian dress. I still wonder what would have happened to those fascinating letters if we hadn't gone in to that room, they would almost certainly have been thrown out during the refurbishment.

In retrospect, this somewhat spooky incident isn't that surprising for Walter Ridpath was one of the most enigmatic patients to have resided at Normansfield and it seems to me he was still trying to attract attention in some way! One of thirteen children, he was born in the City of London on the 12th November 1848 to George and Ann Ridpath. George was a merchant and the family originated in Berwickshire and can be traced back to 1710.

Walter was another of the patients who followed John Langdon Down from Earlswood, initially having been admitted to that Asylum on the 23rd July 1862, aged fourteen. He was then discharged three years later and boarded with the Turner family in Hornsey Rise, North London.

The son of the head of the household, Frederick Turner, was described in the 1881 census as a medical student and it may well be that Frederick was employed at Normansfield. It is possible that Walter was placed with the Turner family in an attempt to rehabilitate him into family life. It is also possible that Walter was able enough to participate in some type of work experience, although the Lunacy Commissioners report (see page 54) would indicate otherwise. Walter had lodged with the Turner family for nearly thirteen years and it seems, on the face it, a real tragedy that he had to return to institutional care.

A document termed *Order for the Reception of a Private Patient* from 20th November 1878 declares that Mrs Elizabeth Turner of Gleadthorpe House, Hornsey Rise is to 'cease caring for Walter' and this was countersigned by Walter's father, George Ridpath, of 67 Finchley New Road, St John's Wood. Walter's brother, Edward Ridpath, gave approval for his hospitalisation.

The 'Commissioners in Lunacy', represented by two doctors, added the following statements:

> *Facts indicating insanity observed by myself; there is no coherence to his discourse - he pronounces words with hesitation but correctly. He is however incoherent on all subjects.*
>
> *He needs to be accompanied when he walks out and indoors. He requires general supervision. He amuses himself in writing in which he is in many respects proficient, and he also occupies himself in needlework.*

Donald Mackintosh, Physician

> *He (Ridpath) is extremely childish - has exalted notions concerning himself and his own affairs and is capable of doing very little that is useful or purposeful. Answers are meaningless and actions are those of an imbecile. He is incapable of walking alone, he becomes conscious and uncomfortable when out of doors. Is inclined to mischief - very peculiar in his habits. Writes his name in every possible place. Has excessive vanity (from Mrs Elizabeth Turner).*

Dr Francis Perry

It is a little confusing that according to the official Normansfield casebook, Walter was not recorded as a patient at the hospital until 20th March 1882. In any case, at the time of his admission to Normansfield, Walter was diagnosed 'healthy' apart from suffering epilepsy and is described as a 'Congenital Idiot'. The fact that he was termed an 'Imbecile at birth' shows that he may already have borne the physical characteristics of Down's syndrome.

The first entry in the patient's casebook is a little more optimistic and somewhat kinder to Walter:

> *Formerly a patient of Dr Down's at Earlswood. He is a well-grown lad. He has little epileptic fits but has not had any lately. He speaks instinctively and with broken sentences. He can read a little and writes very well, but writes in the broken way in which he speaks. He . . . himself is precise in all his ways. He is clean in all his habits. There is no insanity in his family.*

Further entries in the casebooks following his admission occur every month or so and suggest Walter has settled in very happily. He is always reported to be 'happy', 'content', 'in excellent health'. One note states he weighs ten stone.

The Langdon Down Trust archive has yielded a number of letters from Walter to John Langdon Down. This may be unique, since no other examples of direct correspondence between Down and his patients exist. Walter sends neatly printed requests to Dr Down and addresses him affectionately, calling him a 'good man' and signs them 'with Walter's love'. Walter also frequently refers to himself as a 'good, quiet man'.

He seems to want to provide proof of his good behaviour in order to be rewarded with the objects he demands in his letters.

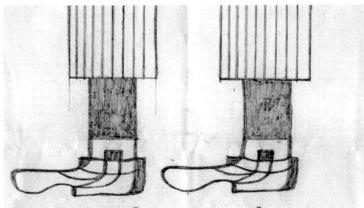

BLUE PAIRS OF SLIPPERS
SMART YOUNG MAN UNCLE
WALTER SAY WORD SHOE'S
MAKER'S.

MR BRIGG'S.

GRIFFIN.	NORMANSFIELD.
MURDER RIDPATH . . .	. . . .
MURDER RIDPATH . . .	. . . .
MURDER RIDPATH . . .	. . . .
MURDER RIDPATH . . .	. . . .

THOSE BOYS BEGAN CALLED SO ARE SILLY
NAME MURDER RIDPATH SO ARE NOT QUITE
MARRIED MAN NOVEMBER 12TH JAMES
RIDPATH NOT LIKE CALLED MURDER RIDPATH IN
HASTINGS SO ARE GOOD MAN; QUIET MAN.
NEW WHIP.

These requests include cotton reels, notepaper, 'new box pencils', 'silver ink new bottle' and envelopes. He also asks for slippers and various items of jewellery, such as a silver watch chain and rings.

Walter's handwriting is exquisite and he produces realistic drawings which record his experiences. In one letter he recalls a trip to the dentist, referring to 'mouth sweet' and 'new tooth good', along with sketches of teeth after the visit.

Some of Walter's correspondence is, however, slightly disjointed and occasionally inexplicable. He mainly refers to himself in the third person and in one letter describes his marital status as 'Not quite married man'. In others, he talks of the other boys teasing him and consequently asks Dr Down for a schoolroom 'by self' as 'Walter Ridpath so good man everyday'. He also describes the boys who evidently bullied him at Normansfield as silly and repeats the phrase 'MURDER RIDPATH' several times.

This bullying is mentioned in a letter from his brother, James, to Mary Langdon Down, dated 16th November 1883, and sent from St Leonard's-on-Sea, Sussex. It was written after Walter had enjoyed a holiday with his family. James Ridpath wrote that his brother:

> . . . complained very much of boys teasing him and gets rather excited when he talks about it. He is, as you are probably aware, of a very sensitive disposition and should be kept as much as possible from this.

Walter Ridpath are
shall come down Hastings
so are quiet man good
look quite nice man
have more Holiday
I send kind regards to
you all,   My Friends,
    I am
Your loving Brother
Walter Ridpath,

There is much correspondence with Mary Langdon Down from all of Walter's siblings, including payments made by Edward Ridpath for Walter's board at the hospital. Most of the letters deal with arrangements for the family to see Walter. They would visit him at

> D͞r Down. wants
> you take poor
> writing desk letters
> case over shop two
> Things for Walter
> Ridpath. to buy
> two New keys not
> having lost things
> in Hastings after
> summer time,

Normansfield and made plans for him to travel to St Leonard's-on-Sea by train. Walter made these journeys on his own, travelling from Charing Cross to St Leonard's station, where he was collected by a one of the extended Ridpath family.

Walter obviously enjoyed these brief holidays away from Normansfield. In several of his letters to Dr Langdon Down he talks of wanting to be back by the seaside with his siblings. He was obviously able to take quite a few seaside holidays while at Normansfield.

Since Walter was subject to a reception order John Langdon Down was not able to give permission for him leave the confines of the hospital without approval from higher authorities. The following is a letter from his brother, dated 27th October 1883:

James Ridpath, St Leonard's-on-Sea

Dear Sir,

I have just written to the Commissioners in Lunacy to ask permission to have Walter down here for a week's holiday – to which he has been looking forward to for a long time – we propose having him down here on the 10th of November – just before his birthday so that he can spend it with us his sister will bring him down here on that day (Saturday).

I am
Dear Sir
Yours truly

James Ridpath

The correspondence between Mary Langdon Down and the Ridpath family is of a very practical nature. It is usually to make visiting arrangements or to confirm that he has received their parcels, or, as in the following, to gently break bad news on their behalf:

October 6th 1885

Dear Mrs Down,

I have had a letter from my brother Walter in which he is evidently looking forward to his usual visit here on his birthday. I write therefore to ask you (that as Mrs Ridpath has been very ill lately, is not at all strong yet) if you would tell him that we will have him down at some future time – tell him this with our love as I know it will be a disappointment to him - but he is reasonable enough, will anticipate his usual ways.

I am yours sincerely

James Ridpath

Walter was also evidently very fond of James's wife, Emily Seymour, to whom he would write regularly. He also sent presents to her from the hospital.

Walter remained happily at Normansfield until his death from pneumonia on 19th October 1909. It is quite remarkable that he should have reached the age of 61 during a time when the life expectancy of a person with Down's Syndrome was just five years. This clearly reflects well on the care received by Walter and the many other patients who lived for years at Normansfield under John Langdon Down's supervision.

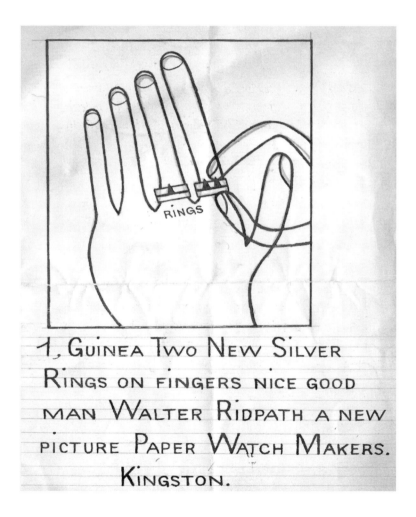

RINGS

1, GUINEA TWO NEW SILVER RINGS ON FINGERS NICE GOOD MAN WALTER RIDPATH A NEW PICTURE PAPER WATCH MAKERS. KINGSTON.

CHAPTER FIVE

A SOMEWHAT MELANCHOLY ESTABLISHMENT

> *If, however, foreign visitors were not particularly charmed with our London streets, they were taken to see a good many forms of English life which, it may be hoped, were not displeasing to them. Some hundreds of them, for instance, were invited by Dr Langdon Down to a garden party at Normansfield, near Hampton Court. This indeed is a somewhat melancholy establishment, for it is, practically speaking, a kind of Earlswood for the wealthier classes, and the scale on which it is conducted cannot fail to awaken mournful reflections.*

The Church Times, 12 August 1881

lmost exactly a year after *The Church Times* noted the scheduled visits for overseas visitors to Normansfield, a young girl by the name of Lucy Ellen Newbald was admitted. Lucy was born in 1871, in Cottingham, Yorkshire, to a wealthy ship owner. Her mother, Mary Ruth Newbald, was described as 'delicate', which turns out to be something of an understatement.

The casebook notes on her arrival that Lucy is aged eleven years old – and single!

> *A delicate girl of the mongolian type . . . rough skin . . . able to walk and talk indistinctly. Feeds with difficulty. Can't read or write.*

Very cheerful and obedient. No bruises. (This observation appears regularly in case books of the era.) No fits or convulsions. No history of insanity.

By September, Lucy had apparently settled in happily and there is a letter from her mother in December 1882:

My dear Mrs Langdon Down,

I have sent off a hamper for dear little Lucy, containing toys, books, dolls and a few eatables. I hope they will arrive safely and that she and the other little children will have a very happy day. I hope all your children keep well this very miserable weather. It must cause you very great anxiety having so many under your care at this time of year.

I am most anxious to know Dr Langdon Down's his opinion of my darling child.

Would you kindly give her this little note,

With kind regards,
Mary Newbald

The following year, both Lucy and her mother were in poor health. So her father writes to Mary Langdon Down:

13th June 1883

Dear madam

I have your post of yesterday and am much grieved to hear of Lucy's illness. I do hope she will improve soon but as I dare not tell my wife in her critical state of health – if Lucy should be in extreme danger and you think it necessary that I should come up please telegraph. It is very difficult for me to leave home at present so that I could only come in case of extreme necessity. I feel quite satisfied that you will do all that can be done for the poor little thing.

With thanks for your kindness I am
Yours truly
C Newbald

Newbald

Westwood,
Beverley.

Dec.ᵣ 14ᵗʰ 1882.

My dear Mrs. Langdon Down
I have sent off a
Hamper, for dear little
Lucy, Containing toys,
Books, Dolls, + a few
Eatables, I hope they will
arrive all safely + that
She + the other little
Children will have a
very happy day—

An even more dismal letter is written within two months and in extraordinary circumstances:

> *16th August 1883*
>
> *My dear madam*
>
> *I am very sorry to inform you that my wife died this morning after a long illness – I hope Lucy is improving but suppose she would scarcely understand if she were told about her mother's death. If I have occasion to visit London I shall certainly come and see her.*
>
> *Yours truly C Newbald*

Two months later, Mr Newbald again corresponds with Mary Langdon Down:

> *8th October 1883*
>
> *My dear madam,*
>
> *It is possible I may have to come to London in a few days and when there I should like to take the opportunity to see little Lucy. I may also bring one of her little sisters with me.*
>
> *Would it be convenient if I called next Friday or Saturday morning?*
>
> *C Newbald*

Lucy resided at Normansfield with regular visits from her father and sisters. In 1885, however, her health started to fail and the following are entries in her medical notes:

> *October 29th: restless in night – bluish – cough.*
>
> *October 31st: very pale temperature 103-104 breathing quick*
> *November 2nd: remains the same, cyanosed.*

And then quite simply:

> *November 3rd: died*

Lucy was aged just 14.

Within a week there was a letter from Mr Newbald:

9th November 1885

I forgot to say anything to you about Lucy's clothes. We should not have liked to have them sent here so perhaps you will kindly give them away to some poor people to whom they would be acceptable. I think this would be the best way of disposing of them.

With kind regards, believe me, yours truly
C Newbald

I hope Mrs Langdon Down is better.

By the time of Lucy Newbald's death, John Langdon Down had abandoned the theory of racial inference in the physical appearance of 'Mongolian Idiots', but in 1866 he had published a paper entitled, *Observations on an Ethnic Classification of Idiots*. The point of the document was to classify the feeble minded and arrange them within various ethnic categories. Drawing from written and photographic material collated at Earlswood, he came to distinguish a group of patients that he described as 'Mongolian'. (Incidentally, John Langdon Down was one of the first medical practitioners to use photography in a hospital setting and is actually reported to have taken his first clinical photographs in 1862.)

Langdon Down described his typical 'Mongolian' child thus:

The hair is not as black as the real Mongol, the face is flat and broad and destitute of prominence, the lips are large and thick, the tongue is long, thick and much roughened, the nose is small, the skin has a slightly yellowish tinge and deficient in elasticity. The boy's aspect is such that it is difficult to realise he is the child of Europeans, but so frequently are these characters presented that there can be no doubt that these ethnic features are the result of degeneration.

He proceeded to categorise the population of the Earlswood asylum into an ethnic hierarchy of 'Mongolian', 'Malay', 'Ethiopian', Aztec' and Caucasian idiots. Although this obviously has racist overtones, it should be placed in a historical context for Anthropologists of the day were grappling with the impact of

Darwin's 1859 *The Origin of the Species* and his revolutionary theory of evolution.

As David Wright says in his book *Mental Disability in Victorian England*:

> To our ears, although Down's suggestion that Caucasians were more 'developed' (in evolutionary terms) than 'Mongols' is offensive, his views actually placed him in the 'liberal' camp of thought. That is, with all those who believed that all races stood on the same continuum and shared common ancestry.

Professor Ward is actually of the opinion that Langdon Down was ambivalent about Darwinism and uncomfortable that it was being used by some to justify racial discrimination. Langdon Down himself was of the opinion that the human race was universal and he stated that 'these examples of the result of degeneracy among mankind appear to me to furnish some arguments in favour of the unity of the human species'.

From his work at Earlswood, John Langdon Down reported that:

> The Mongolian type of idiocy occurs in more than 10% of the cases which are presented to me – they are always congenitally based and never the result of from accidents after uterine life. They have considerable power of imitation even bordering on being mimics. They are humorous and a lively sense of the ridiculous colours their mimicry . . . the co-ordinating faculty is abnormal, but not so defective that it cannot be greatly strengthened . . . the circulation is feeble and however much advance is made intellectually in the summer, some amount of retrogression may be expected in the winter.

It is unlikely that some kind of seasonal malaise caused the parents of Norman MacDonald Borthwick to seek Normansfield's care for their son, but it was indeed in February 1877 that he was admitted to the hospital.

The casebook describes him as male, nine years old, short with fair hair and 'oblique eyes of mongolian type' His circulation was termed as 'feeble' and his general condition as 'normal'. The notes continue:

Norman has had defective mental powers since birth and has no speech. He is obstinate, shy and self willed to the last degree. He is occasionally dirty in his habits and has no reading and writing. He possesses no deformities or bruises and suffers no fits.

Within a couple of months of his admission, Norman was attending the 'kindergarten' and was already settling in well and making some progress:

1877 April 1st, greatly improved speaks answers to questions, plays with others, started to learn to read.

In the next few years, references were made to Norman's 'improved physical and mental health'. His mother was very grateful for the way that her 'Mac' was being cared for and he seemed to make a number of visits back to the family home in Kensington:

10th February 1882

Dear Mrs Down

If Mac is well and a good boy we would like very much to have him home for a little. I will send for him on Friday next if agreeable to you and keep him for a week or 10 days . . . he goes back to school so happily always and is so good and quiet at home now, it is quite a pleasure to see him. His writing we think improved with every letter it seems to us that muscular power to hold the pen steady must be greater.

M E Borthwick

27 Stanhope Gardens
Queens Gate SW

10th June 1883

Dear Mrs Down

I have received your memorandum for Mac and will send things as soon as possible. I should like to have him home for a little it is so long since we have seen him we have had so much to do and think about – some day after the 20th of this month I should like to send for him, but will write again the exact day. I enclose a note for him and wonder how much he understands of what I say to him. His own writing is very much improved and I can never be thankful enough for all you have done for him.

With kind regards
Most truly yours
M E Borthwick

There are also frequent mentions of his weight, which seems to give Mrs Borthwick concern as far as it affected Mac's attire. She also endures frustrating problems with her own staff!

I am so sorry about Mac's clothes but the maid who used to attend to him at home left us lately and I was not able myself to look after the packing of his box. Some things were sent before your note – the others will follow next week. I have given one of his sisters the charge of his things for the future so I hope you will not again be inconvenienced.

I am perplexed about what size of suit to get for Mac, without some list of measurement could you send me the length of trousers and size of waist, length of coat from middle of the back to waist and down the back.

Very sorry to give you so much trouble.

I am so sorry about the trouble Mac's suit has given you it has just arrived. It will be much better to have his other trousers made as you propose by the village tailor. I will have it altered and returned.

*Can you recommend me a cook I am losing one who has been with
me for 10 years – is obliged to go home. I am so sorry for myself.
Since I last wrote I have been laid up with such a bad attack of
neuralgia that I am ordered out of town at once and I have never
been able to get Mac's visit or order his suit. The note you sent me
with the tailors' address having been mislaid while I was in bed.
Will you be so kind as to order a suit from him of a suitable tweed
for about £2.10.0 or so, that was the price of the last and tell the
man to send his bill to me, also the three visits he needs I am sorry
to give you this extra trouble but I have now been four weeks laid
up and I am afraid he must want things at once. I hope you have
not suffered from this long cold winter.*

M E B

By December 1887, the family's circumstances have changed and
when Mrs Borthwick writes requesting a visit from Mac, she states
she would have liked him to stay longer but that she is in lodgings
and has to consider 'the awkwardness of my circumstances':

21st May 1888

Dear Mrs Down

*We have been very uncomfortable here this winter in many ways so
have taken a little house at Fulham as a sort of compromise between
town and country. There is a little garden and fine old trees and
other gardens to be seen which will be a relief from bricks and mortar
which I have never loved. Our girls will be able to get up to the
school of cookery where they work. We go next week so after the
1st June our address will be 4 Fulham Park Road.*

   *It will be much easier to have a little visit from Mac there than
here and he will enjoy it more too. Normansfield must be very
pretty now and everybody must be enjoying the lovely weather in
your pretty grounds. I enclose a little note for Mac.*

With kindest regards to you and Dr Down.

Nearly ten years later, Norman is still returning to the family home
for visits and in the following letter Mrs Borthwick refers to Queen
Victoria's sixtieth Jubilee:

23rd June 1897

Dear Mrs Down,

With your consent I would like to have Mac home on Monday next for a visit. I will come for him in the forenoon unless I hear to the contrary. What a wonderful day yesterday was in the history of our country. I am sure you agree with me that what so ever our private sorrows we can rejoice over god's good gift to us of a sovereign who more than any before her has lived in the spirit of the words, 'O man what is good and what doth the Lord require of thee but to do justly and love mercy and to walk humbly with thy God.'

 I thoroughly enjoyed seeing the procession (from the stand in the constitution Hill) every detail of which was most interesting and impressive especially the representative men from all the ends of the earth. Mr Borthwick and I had no intention of going but had tickets given us only two days before and I feel so glad we were able to join in such a wonderful demonstration.

Hoping to see you all on Monday.
ME Borthwick

13 Markham Sq
Chelsea
SW

21st July 1897

Dear Mrs Down,

I enclose a cheque for £20 to place against Mac's a/c. We have been enjoying a short stay with our daughter Mrs MacDonald and our two little granddaughters in most delightful country near Liphook.
 I am sorry to say they leave soon for Egypt.

Hoping this will find you and yours well

MEB

There are no more letters regarding Norman Borthwick, just a couple of the hospital's usual updates. Inevitably there is attention to his weight in February 1915:

Gained 7lbs, now 9 stone 7lbs, continues in good health, works in the garden and amuses himself with writing. He is happy and gives no trouble.

A month later, his sister called to see him and Norman is reported in good health and taking 'thyroid extract'. This is particularly interesting in that it was actually only discovered in the 1970's that a high percentage of people with Down's syndrome suffer from a thyroid disorder.

In June, Norman holidayed in Reigate. Sadly this is the last entry that can be found for 'Mac' and so it must be assumed that Norman Borthwick remained at Normansfield until his death.

It is interesting to consider why children and adults with Down's syndrome were not identified before John Langdon Down's work: Conor Ward stated that in Shakespeare's time it has been estimated there were no more than 100 people with Down's syndrome in the whole of England and by the middle of the 19th century, only about half the women in England reached the age of 35, beyond which the incidence of Down's syndrome increases. It was also more than likely that they would remain in seclusion and die young. There was, after all, a high general mortality rate in children.

In 1887, John Langdon Down was invited to deliver a series of lectures by the Medical Society of London. These were known as *The Lettsomian Lectures* and in the first of these Langdon Down referred to the early history of children burdened by what he described as 'mental alienation' or 'mental incapacity'. They had been placed in the category of idiots and regarded as beyond help. He established the distinction between 'idiots' and 'imbeciles', and commented that he preferred the term 'feeble minded'. 'I have no great liking for the term idiot,' he wrote. 'It is so frequently a name of reproach.'

In his second lecture, Langdon Down described various factors that seemed to have caused or contributed to the disability in some of his patients. These ranged from sunstroke, the excessive use of opium (frequently used in the treatment of children at that time), the excessive drinking habits of parents, and finally to the possibility of sexual abuse which he felt might lead to impaired psychological development.

He also referred to maternal problems in pregnancy, either

through ill health or unhappiness. Certainly, a number of his patients at Normansfield had mothers who were described as 'delicate', which may have influenced this hypothesis.

Within three years, John Langdon Down's own health had begun to fail, although he continued to work through the first half of the 1890's. On 7th October 1896 he had planned to visit his Harley Street consulting rooms, but shortly after breakfast, before he had left Normansfield, he suddenly collapsed. His son, Reginald, attended him, but Dr Down died very quickly. The death certificate noted 'a sudden heart attack' as the cause of death.

The doctor had given instructions that he was to be cremated. His coffin was transported to Waterloo Station and then transferred by train to Woking Crematorium. The following morning a funeral service was held in the theatre at Normansfield. According to Conor Ward:

> *When his funeral procession passed through Kingston the pavements were lined with people standing in silent respect. Shops were closed and blinds drawn. So many floral tributes had been received that a separate landau was needed to convey them. Mary Langdon Down could not face the public ceremony. Her distress was overwhelming and she sat in the vestry alone with her sister-in-law, devastated by the intensity of her grieving.*

The British Medical Journal's obituary reported:

> *By the time of his death he was a national and international expert on the mental diseases of childhood and youth, and a prominent and respected member of the British medical establishment. He remained a Consulting Physician to the London Hospital until his death. Down was also involved in local politics and administration, being appointed a Justice of the Peace for Westminster and Middlesex, a County Alderman and remaining to his death 'a prominent liberal.*

John Langdon Down's influence and enlightened views stretched beyond his work at Normansfield. He was an opponent of slavery, supported women's right to vote (his Harley Street consulting rooms were used for fundraising by the Suffragette movement)

A bust of the pioneering John Langdon Down, a copy of which is exhibited at the Langdon Down Trust centre in the old hospital building.

and was supportive of feminine admission to most professions such as the law and clergy, but somewhat surprisingly opposed the admission of women to medical school.

Dr John Langdon Down was a true pioneer in his field, devising innovative and creative activities for the life-enrichment of those in his care. Staff were trained in the use of sensory stimulation and 'role playing' practical tasks and even early forms of 'work experience' were sought in the hope that a few patients might be able to return to their family homes and lead some kind of independent life outside the institution.

Developing educational opportunities for children with learning disabilities (100 years before it became government policy) and by using music and drama as therapeutic tools, Langdon Down treated each patient as an individual, whose unique potential needed to be detected and nurtured.

CHAPTER SIX

A VERY FINE DAY FOR A FUNERAL

At all events, Dr Down has at last attained his ideal: he has acquired an establishment where everything which he could have idealised has been realised and where even now an ample measure of well deserved success has accrued to him.

Medical Times, 28th June 1879

Florence Thornton was admitted to Normansfield on 8th March 1886, and was described as:

A child of mongolian type with feeble circulation. Very imitative and affectionate . . . knows most of her letters . . . speech indistinct. Clean in her habits. No history of insanity in family . . . no convulsion or epilepsy.

Florence was aged just seven when she was moved from the family home in Putney to Normansfield, an event that must have been extraordinarily painful for all concerned. It would appear that Florence's admission, as with many others, resulted from the ill health of her mother, Mary, who wrote an emotional letter to Mary Langdon Down two days after Florence's arrival:

We were quite excited to hear she had settled down so happily and I am more thankful than I can express that she is under your kind care – for I know she will receive every care and kindness with refinement I have had many an anxious thought for her knowing that I have but 4 years to live and she may be spared for many . . .

my great hope is that everything that can be done for her. I feel happy in knowing that this will now be the case.

Despite the fact that she was married to a doctor, it's not clear how Mrs Thornton was able to predict her own mortality quite so precisely – perhaps it was due to her religious conviction – a trait of which Mary Langdon Down would have thoroughly approved.

We can gain an insight into the genteel Thornton upbringing from a letter written the day after Florence moved to Teddington:

I forgot to mention that she has been accustomed to be put to bed every day at 12 o'clock and taken up again at 1 o'clock also that she has always been with us in the morning at family prayer and behaves as well as we do ourselves and she always clasps her hands during grace at meals and says amen – she has too kneeled down by my side at the end and repeated after me, "pray God bless Flo . . . etc". She likes to do these things and I like her to do them, so that when she is better she may remember it all and continue it all.

Florence Thornton soon after her admission to Normansfield in 1886.

Mary Thornton was also a woman of organisational capability (another characteristic of her Normansfield namesake) although there may have been some displacement activity involved:

I sent off my little Flo's trunk this afternoon though very imperfectly filled I altered two pairs of drawers and shall be glad to hear if they are nice and comfortable and if they are I will alter the rest for her before sending them to you – if they do not . . . I will get new ones for her. I will send the rest of her wardrobe as soon as possible she requires more pinafores and handkerchiefs. I will make her another dress so that she can caste off the one she had when I took her to you. That was only her morning frock to which I intended her to caste off.

I have sent her very old doll as I thought that she would feel more at home with it. I hope she did not fret for us when she found that we were gone. I dare say she is quite at home already. I think I should have told you that my husband is in the Bengal army when you asked me if we had any title. Trusting you will excuse this long letter.

Mary

Mary Langdon Down must have been moved for she replied immediately to the delight of Mary Thornton who reciprocated on 10th March 1886:

Your kind little note received this morning was such a sweet surprise for I really did not expect you to write feeling sure your duties must be managed and arduous so that you must be very tired at the end of the day.

Thank you so much for giving the news of darling Florence. I am glad she remembered Dr Langdon Down. I am sure she will love him for he is so kind. I hope she made her bow to him when she left the room. She has become accustomed when leaving the drawing room in the evening to go round, say good night and then when she reached the door and turn round and give a low bow.

I enclose her labels.

Mary

Mrs Thornton came to see Mary soon after admission and visited regularly. More importantly, Florence also spent time with her mother and siblings in Putney and Mary was pleased with her daughter's progress, 'I thought her improved last time I saw her'.

She continued, however, to be concerned with Florence's accoutre:

> *8th May 1886*
>
> *I sent the two cotton frocks, a garden hat and a cloak also a little petticoat to try, for I noticed when she came home that the petticoats I sent her had no fit in them at all. I rather fancy the one I now send will be too small but it is only on approval so that if it does not do it can be changed. I hope the cloak will be right but I cannot tell as it had not come when Flo went back. I will send more frocks and some flannel petticoats next week and a hat for walking. If the frocks are too long perhaps you will kindly have tucks made in them.*
>
> *Mary T*

> *1st June 1886*
>
> *When you are sending the little ones to the seaside I should like Flo to go with them, please – the sea air does her much good. Flo loves to catch the waves. I hope she is quite well again she had a cold when I saw her last and looked a little pale from it. I hope to go and see her on Thurs next as I shall be unable to on Sat. What ever may be necessary for her in the way of clothing for the seaside I will get for her if you will kindly let me know. She will want a strong secure hat.*
>
> *Mary Thornton*

Mary Thornton was obviously devoted to Florence as there are a number of letters displaying her love and affection for her daughter:

> *I would like to take one more peep at my darling Flo before she leaves for the seaside and I will go over to Normansfield tomorrow if all be well.*

And then:

I should like to know if the little ones have returned from the seaside trip as I am quite longing to see my darling again and if she is at Normansfield, I would like to go to see her next Saturday afternoon.

Mary was obviously delighted with the care that Florence was receiving at Normansfield for she recommends the hospital to several other mothers:

Would you kindly forward me by post a prospectus. A friend of mine was telling me of a lady whose daughter suffered from epilepsy and weak intellect and I told her I thought Normansfield would be just the place for her so she has asked me for a prospectus.

Florence seemed to be in robust health for her first few months at the hospital, but contracted whooping cough, which naturally concerned her mother:

24th August 1886

Dear Mrs L-D

Thank you for letting me know of dear Flo having the Whooping Cough poor pet. I hope she will have it mildly. It is a distressing illness . . . all my other children had it recently . . . I hope it will not leave Flo delicate for the winter. I noticed she wheezed very much when she coughed when I was with her on Friday last and she looked very pale. I am quite sure she will be very well taken care of so that I am quite comfortable about her although I shall feel a little anxious until the worst of it is over for with all the care and kindness in the world these things sometimes will leave bad effects. I suppose I should not come to see her for a time? I can quite fancy her little eyes looking weak from the coughing. Give her a kiss and tell her I am so sorry for her suffering. She will understand that I think.

Kind regards
believe me
yours truly
Mary Thornton

Several missives mention how Mary Thornton's visits to see Florence were thwarted by inclement weather. At times Mary seems quite obsessed by the elements:

17th October 1886

Started to see Flo on Sat but the rain was so heavy I was obliged to return home. . .

27th November 1886

I quite intended going to see Flo today but the fog was so thick that I thought it unwise to venture. . . I will try to get to Hampton Wick soon but shall not do so while there are dense fogs.

29th June 1887

Cheque £28.11.0 on a/c

Dear Flo, I am so pleased the dear lambs are enjoying the sea air. It must be refreshing to them this hot weather.

9th December 1887

I hope to see Florence tomorrow, if the weather is fine . . .

Tired with excessive heat . . . do not venture out in the evening.

However, whatever the weather Florence's wardrobe was still a matter of importance to her mother;

I sent off two knitted petticoats by train – the jacket came but had to be returned as they made it of a much lighter shade of plum and it would not have looked well with the dark bonnet – it is very tiresome for they have been so long making the one and will I expect be equally long making another. I am sending by the post a pair of sleeping socks for Flo. They are ugly but I hope will be comfortable.

Mary

There is also a letter from Florence's sister, Nellie, who reiterates the Thornton family's passion for fashion:

I shall come over to see Flo tomorrow afternoon. Will you let her wear her pretty frock with the steel trimming as one of my cousins is coming with me and looks better in that than anything.

'Poor dear Flo', pictured shortly before her death.

The photograph of Florence certainly shows quite how elegantly Florence was dressed. Mary was clearly delighted with the result:

Dear Mrs Langdon Down,

Your kind letter and Flo's photograph were forwarded to me . . . yesterday. I am delighted with the photo and think it a very faithful likeness of the child. She looks as if she were wondering what the photographer was doing. I should like to have six copies please. I think Dr Thornton will be very pleased when he sees the photo.

In fact, the two Marys seem to have struck a firm friendship, Mary Thornton is always concerned with Mary Langdon Down's health, general welfare and onerous responsibilities:

> *I suppose you saw the procession of the Queen's Jubilee. I hope you were not greatly fatigued by it but most people seemed rather tired after it. However, it was worth it I fancy.*

9

MATRON'S DUTIES.

1.—To see that each new house-servant is furnished with a copy of the rules for servants.

2.—To furnish servants with all necessary implements and materials, and to reclaim the same on their leaving.

3.—To be ready for duty at 6-30 a.m., and to see that all house, kitchen, work-room, and private servants are also ready at that time, making the entry in the time-book *there and then*, and informing each servant when *L.* or *Late* is marked against them.

4.—To take the entire oversight of the house-servants, see that they and the men-servants are fully occupied in duty hours, and overlook all domestic work done by the attendants ~~and nurses.~~ To arrange for the evening work till 8 p.m., both of men and maids.

5.—To give special attention to the ventilation, lighting, and shading of the house.

6.—To supervise the cleanliness of the ~~whole house,~~ N *vll* and Hope Villa when cleaned by supers. For this purpose it is necessary to visit every part of the ~~house~~ each *N. W* day. The rooms and corridors appointed for each day's cleaning should be visited *during* and *after* the cleaning, and a report of repairs of any kind that are wanted brought to Mrs. Langdon-Down, or entered in the artizans' books.

In turn, Mary Langdon Down helped Mary Thornton's son, Ted, find employment with W. Plume Solicitors. One area that would have met with Mary Langdon Down's disapproval was, however, the tardy settling of the accounts which seems to have emanated from financial difficulties rather than disorganisation, despite Mary Thornton's protestations:

Cheque £27.2.6d.

I think that is the correct amount but I am not sure for I am **ashamed** *to say the a/c got mislaid. It arrived amongst numbers of Christmas cards and I fear got carried off with some of them for I am unable to find it. If there is any more I will send it to you. Will you kindly let me know. I am so sorry to be troublesome but the a/c being lost has been quite an accident owing to the haste of Christmas.*

Mary

Also:

Pleasure cheque £4.1.3d for Flo's a/c.

I am sorry it is so late this time but unforeseen circumstances prevented me sending it sooner.

And again:

I have not settled the quarterly a/c yet, but will send you a cheque early next month.

By 1899, Mrs Thornton's health seems to have deteriorated. She refers to herself as more of an invalid, and moved to Hove from where her visits are inevitably less regular. She is unable to celebrate Florence's birthday with her:

Kindly get a cake for her birthday which falls on the 21st. I have always had a 6/- sultana cake iced and coated. If you will get one at the same price I will be much obliged.

Sadly, Florence herself, was also in failing health, although other family members are thriving:

> *Sorry to hear of Flo's illness . . . received her letters telling me of her birthday party and how she was looking forward to Christmas. Poor darling, I hope she may be well enough. My daughter-in-law has given us another grandchild today, a fine boy. Both are doing well.*

> *22nd December 1899*

> *Very much thanks dear Mrs Down for the kind letter with glad news of dear Flo convalescence received this morning. We have been thinking of your large party today making merry. I am glad you have not many ill at this time. I have despatched a puzzle by prepaid post today for dear Flo. I thought if she is not well enough to exert her brain with putting it together she might just look at the picture. I will send something later on. We have sent no cards this year for we had no time or heart to select them. We hope to send New Year cards I am enclosing the usual little gift for Flo's nurse if you will kindly give it – as I do not know her name.*

> *Mary*

> *2nd January 1900*

> *I have duly read your kind reports of dear Flo which have given me much comfort and I am pleased she is able to sit up and is concerned with the puzzle. I trust you have not thought me unappreciative of your goodness in sending me the cheering news of her. The reason of my silence is that I have been too ill to write. I am still an invalid. Thank you very much for letting Flo send the Xmas card. Give her our love and kisses for them. We also give thanks for your kind New Year wishes.*

Florence's recovery was unfortunately temporary. Her sister, Nellie, wrote to say:

> *How sorry and grieved we are to learn of her relapse. Influenza makes everything uncertain . . . poor child, she seems just now very delicate – susceptible to any change in temperature. We are quite confident you will take very care of her and so leave her to your administration relying on your skill and care under God.*

On 19th January, Mary Thornton received a telegram that Florence was very unwell. She was evidently too ill to visit her daughter but wrote that, 'We must now bow in submission to our Lord.' There must have been further communication because the following day Dr Thornton telegraphed the hospital that he would come at once. Sadly neither God nor even the administrations of the Langdon Downs could save poor Florence and she died on 20th January 1900. Nellie wrote immediately:

> *Your news this morning was very sad and mother is distressed a good deal about poor little Flo, but I am thankful to say she is bearing it more bravely than I expected. She has been really ill with a bronchial attack else she would have written to you herself. We all send our kindest regards and heartfelt thanks for all your care of Flo. Your letters are so full of motherly sympathy (and) are all very consoling.*
>
> *Nellie Thornton*

Needless to say Mary wrote to Mary Langdon Down on 22nd January:

> *Thank you dear Mrs Down for your kind letter received this morning. We were glad to hear that your household is once more restored to health I trust you are now quite well. I have been thinking much of you I hoped to hear soon that all was well again but it has indeed been a trying and hard winter for all. With regard to my dear Flo's clothes and belongings I should like them to be sent here if not giving too much trouble.*
>
> *Dear Flo, I never can realise that she is still not with you. I have been so long accustomed when thinking of her to see her in my imagination . . . to joyously meet and welcome us, but it is well with her now. I must learn to think of her in her bright new home. My interest in Normansfield will not cease with her removal,*
>
> *We are wishful also to know what our indebtedness to you is as we shall be pleased to send you a cheque. My husband has a memo which was sent in December but he thought it better to have a fresh one as there may be other items for you to add since that one was made out.*

Within a week, Dr James Howard Thornton also expressed his gratitude to Mary Langdon Down:

28th January 1900

My dear Mrs Down

I write a few lines to thank you from my heart for all your care and kindness to our poor little Flo during the 14 years of her residence at Normansfield. Now that she has passed away it is a great comfort to us all to feel that her life was as bright and happy as it could have been under the circumstances of her case. We also wish to thank your sons for their care and attention of her during her final illness.

We fortunately had a very fine day for the funeral. We had selected a beautiful spot in Hove cemetery for her grave and there she was laid to rest. The cemetery is not very far from our house so Mrs Thornton will be able to visit the spot without difficulty when the weather has grown milder but she was not able to attend the funeral.

I am sending you a copy of my book 'Memories of 7 Campaigns' which I hope you will accept as a small token of our regard for you and our gratitude for your truly motherly care of our poor little girl.

With kindest regards from us all
J H Thornton

The final letter from Mary Thornton to Normansfield was posted on 15th March 1900. The grieving continued, but the gratitude and appreciation had been fully expressed. There was just one matter that needed addressing:

I am enclosing a cheque for £30 now and to ask you if you will mind very much waiting until 16th of May for the remaining portion of the a/c for dear Flo as my husband has had calls upon him unexpectedly which have made him rather short this quarter and on the 15th May his pension becomes due when it will be all the more convenient to him to settle the last. I am so sorry not to be able to send the whole amount at once but as you have already been kind I feel you will in this case. I hope you are all very well.

Mary

CHAPTER SEVEN

WAITING
IN THE WINGS

Tis not an aimless pleasure we pursue;
Much higher purpose we have in view:

To wake the senses stricken in their birth,
To rouse dull apathy to harmless mirth,

To fix the attention by a word or sound,
And bring back reason at a single bound:

To pacify the irritable child,
And watch the sufferer of its pain beguiled.

To bring light into the vacant eye,
And cheer the hearts of those more prone to cry;

Distract the thoughts of those who pine for home,
And touch some chord in minds that seem o'erthrown.

For soothing care that all misfortunes bring,
We feel with Hamlet that 'the play's the thing.

This prologue, written by a member of the Normansfield staff, rumoured to be one of the orchestra members, was delivered by John Langdon Down at an 1887 Normansfield concert, ten years after work had begun on the new entertainment hall.

Roland Plumbe, whose relative had been a resident at Earslwood, was an old friend of the Langdon Downs and was employed as architect. He had, in fact, no experience of designing theatres and was principally known as being chief architect of the London

Hospital – another link to John Langdon Down. The building was totally new, the hall erected on the first floor level of the hospital and the ground floor used as a children's play area.

The formal opening of the hall on 27th June 1879 by the Earl of Devon was a prestigious occasion with Dr Langdon Down arranging for a private train to bring his guests from Waterloo to Hampton Wick. The stage-struck Langdon Downs were fascinated by theatre and John Langdon Down saw 'Mongolian' children as being particularly open to playmaking and performance, as evidenced in his Lettsomian Lecture:

> *They have a strong sense of the ridiculous. Often they will talk to themselves . . . they in fact go through a play in which the patient, doctor, governess and nurses are the dramatis personae – a play in which the patient is represented as defying and contravening the wishes of those in authority.*

Langdon Down used these ideas as a form of therapy and training for the patients at Normansfield, as described by Francesca Byrne in her thesis, *Dr Langdon Down and the Normansfield Theatre*:

> *The Langdon Downs fostered an inclusive environment where both patients, staff, cooperated in their theatrical endeavours . . . The idea of voyeurism was still at work in asylums such as Bethlem during the nineteenth century, but at Normansfield the asylum inmates were no longer viewed as objects of curiosity and fear; they were both performers and audience mixing with the local community and all experiencing the same excitement provided for their amusement and education.*

According to Francesca Byrne, every Thursday evening there was the opportunity for any patient or staff member who so wished to sing, dance, recite or act together or as solo performers. A visit by a Dr Cheyne Brady noted that:

> *The pupils sang hymns together and several were taught to play musical instruments and in summer this band performs once a week on the terrace, and fetes are held at which games of agility are practised, and processions of the pupils, rendered gay by flags and banners, perform evolutions to the sound of merry music.*

In order to use the drama and music as a form of treatment, it was vital that the staff who were to be employed at Normansfield were not only skilled attendants, but also possessed theatrical talent – a sort of therapeutic Butlins where the staff, although not exactly 'Redcoats', should be either able to play an instrument or sing. Attendants, recruited through employment agencies, thus had to have some performing talent and it was Mary Langdon Down who pursued suitable candidates to ensure that all the staff were appropriately qualified in this respect.

Requests to employment agencies requesting such accomplished staff were duly made, with varying success. A letter from 'Hill and Courtneys' bureau in December 1897 declared:

> *We regret that up to the present we have not been able to send you a musician attendant, but we know of a young man who would suit you very well. He has a nursing certificate.*

In February the following year, they apologised for the fact that they did not have a violin player on their books at the present time!

Mary Langdon Down must have been successful in her quest to locate musicians with a social conscience, however – let's face it, no

The Normansfield staff band.

mean feat in any era – for the Normansfield staff orchestra grew ultimately to an impressive ensemble of sixteen members. They were, by all accounts, more than competent and performed regularly in the theatre. Once the hall had been built and theatrical performances were planned, Mary Langdon Down extended her already onerous duties by becoming stage manager which she, no doubt, fulfilled with her usual administrative zeal. Other family members also participated in the plays and cabarets. The Downs' children, Reginald and Percival, later appeared with the Cambridge Footlights, and in 1889 performed a duet together which revealed their medical background:

> *Squire, our inmates are happy in spite of their ills, 'Impossible!*
> *The fact, I assure you. Hugely we find music and dancing much*
> *better than pills.*

The highlight of Normansfield's social calendar was always the Christmas pantomime, written by the Langdon Downs and repeated on two successive evenings for the residents of Hampton Wick. The panto was the start of the traditional festivities that were such a feature of life at Normansfield. An edition of *The Surrey Comet* in January 1875 enthused:

> *The Christmas and New Year's theatrical entertainment was*
> *repeated on Wednesday evening to a number of the residents in the*
> *village. The elegant well-equipped little theatre attached to the*
> *establishment was prettily decorated by the patients. The philosophy,*
> *as well as the humanity, of the principle so well expressed in this*
> *passage no one will doubt nowadays. Kindness is a potent element*
> *in the remedial treatment pursued at Normansfield, and the success*
> *which attended Dr Down's efforts bears ample testimony, were any*
> *needed, to the justness of the principle upon which his system is*
> *founded.*
>
> *The pieces selected ere, as may well be imagined, by no means*
> *of a sentimental or tragic kind, but broad, screaming farces, with*
> *plenty of laughter moving situations in which people were found*
> *under tables and beds - ay, and in beds sometimes – under the most*
> *ludicrous and perplexing circumstances, and in which the reckless*
> *destruction to property that goes on is frightful to contemplate.*

Although reviews were generally kind to the Normansfield staff in these amateur productions, *The Kingston and Surbiton News* reported in 1883 that:

> *Mr Habgood played Vivian Thornbrake a young squire and in another 'burlesque' Rumtifoozle (an exiled Bounding Brigand) and seemed far more happy as Rumtifoozle than he had been as a young squire in the farce.*

Normansfield actually had its own press and published a journal entitled *Our Magazine* which included a number of articles about life at Normansfield. The inaugural edition was printed in May 1908:

> *Our first issue presents favourable opportunity for a few words about our weekly entertainments of the season just past 1907-08. To say that we have looked forward to and afterwards heartily enjoyed them is not as much as they deserve. We claim that the concerts of this season have been quite up to the standard of the previous years and that generally great praise is due to all our kind friends who have each contributed to this issue. We take this opportunity of tendering to all of these friends our heartiest thanks coupled with our desire of a continuance of this kind next winter.*
>
> *We have been delighted with all these but we have stamped particularly in our memories the 'Conifers' entertainment when the officers of the house introduced the sketch entitled, 'Miss Flippers Holiday'.*
>
> *The 'Trematon' entertainment of 2nd April deserves a special word or two of praise from us, for not only did the 'Trematonians' produce a farcical sketch, 'Mrs Bentbone's Trouble', but it was written by a Trematonian Mr E H Miles and altogether that gentleman and his able helpers very great credit. We add 'Bravo Miles', may this encourage you to future endeavours. We shall certainly expect to hear from you next season.*
>
> *While now looking forward to our out-of-door sports which a genial summer should afford us, we shall be fully prepared late, to hail the approach of the entertainment season 1908-09.*

We can imagine from the slightly patronising tone of the description and the manner of the exhorting praise that Mr Miles was actually one of the patients, although there is some debate as to how much the residents actually played a part in the entertainments. Despite the fact that a few of the roles were played by patients, it was usually the attendants who took the principal parts. The talents of the staff members were also employed at other occasions, such as Reginald Langdon Down's coming of age and also the celebration of the Queen Victoria's 50th Jubilee in 1887, when festivities were held at Normansfield. *The Surrey Comet* reported that:

> *Old as well as young found much amusement . . . and the children had caught a glimpse of the fairyland into which the charming grounds were transformed with variegated lamp. Dancing was pursued with energy upon the turf to the strains of the well trained band of the institution.*

John and Mary Langdon Down were of the belief that 'winter evenings should be made cheerful with concerts dancing and dramatic representations'. The couple were also linked with the local Genesta Amateur Dramatic Club, who contributed with plays and light operas to the Normansfield varieties. Productions such as *She Stoops to Conquer*, *The Gondoliers* and *The Pirates of Penzance* were performed at the theatre from 1891. After eighteen years the

The Genesta Players production of Gilbert & Sullivan's 'The Gondoliers'. Normansfield 1897.

'Red Rider'. The production of 1896, performed at Normansfield.

GADC moved to the Surbiton Assembly Rooms and by 1927, its membership had increased substantially. The Genesta served as a stepping stone to the professional stage for a number of actors and the world famous playwright R C Sherriff premiered one of his pieces *Mr Birdy's Finger* with the GADC – a play that in due course transferred to the West End.

The profile of the Genesta could have been further raised if a request by Edward Habgood (he of 'Rumtifoozle' fame and a master at Normansfield from 1880 to 1883) to his friend George Bernard Shaw had been accepted to join him as an assistant master! The Genesta Club remained active well in to the 1950's and was a valuable and credible theatrical influence within the community.

Mary Langdon Down's fondness for Gilbert and Sullivan actually resulted in the acquisition of a series of six life-size portraits which were hung on the walls of the auditorium. It has been established that these were painted for the first production of Gilbert and Sullivan's *Ruddigore* at the Savoy Theatre in 1887. The portraits were stored in the Museum of London for many years but are now back in situ and continue to provide a sense of historical decoration at the theatre.

John Earl, former director of the Theatres Trust, describes the amusement hall as:

. . . a remarkably complete and rare survival of a private theatre in
the 1870s and in the top ten percentage of all listed buildings.

It is indeed a somewhat surprising building because from the outside it does not look like a traditional Victorian theatre. The edifice has flat chapel-like windows and is approached by an internal corridor. In fact there is something Narnia-esque about the entrance to the hall, as one has to open a normal sized wooden door to reveal the expansive interior and large stage. John Earl also described the theatre as possessing, 'an ecclesiastical air'. This is not surprising because, apart from theatrical productions, the building performed another major function throughout most of its existence – that of a church to staff and residents. Its gothic decorative style is almost unique for a theatre and the Sunday service here was an important event in the week's activities for many years. One of the theatre's backdrops incorporated the Apostles' Creed and the Lord's Prayer and residents could practice their reading at rehearsals for the service which were held midweek.

In terms of the actual style of the theatre, the proscenium is designed in an eclectic manner, richly coloured and gilded and the original decorations have survived almost intact. It is embellished with gothic frames containing four life size painted figures of 'Tragedy', 'Painting', 'Music' and 'Comedy' and above these are portraits of classical dramatists, including William Shakespeare. The door panels are gilt edged and are painted with a variety of foliage and exotic birds such as a stork and a flamingo. Extreme care had been taken over the lighting system, incorporating a gas burner that contained light fittings, ventilator and gas footlights for the stage. The Langdon Downs also had an elaborate heating system installed in order to provide a professional approach – not to mention some comfort for the audience.

According to the Theatres Trust, the theatre contains the finest and rarest collection of watercolour stock scenery in Britain. There are splendid backdrops and painted cloths, stock scenery of a woodland scene, a baronial hall, a garden, half-timbered houses, a parlour and two kitchens. Sadly, as the theatre became neglected down the years, these backdrops (and many more painted backcloths, borders and tall scenic flats which were stored behind

'All the world's a stage' – as well as backdrops and stock scenery.

the stage) required serious conservation work and, in 1997, the whole lot was salvaged by the Textile Conservation Centre for the Theatres Trust and removed from the site for safekeeping.

The Textile Conservation Centre, now based at the Winchester Campus of the University of Southampton, conducted a painstaking project to conserve the unique painted scenery between 2003 and

2005. Damaged areas of the canvas were strengthened with patches or backings of Japanese paper or linen fabric. Painted patches were used to fill in the missing colour in holes and tears, but details of the design were not restored.

Although much more work remains to be done, the condition of the scenery has been stabilised and it has now been returned to the theatre to a purpose built store in the basement. Sadly it is too fragile to use today, but originally the flats or stock scenery (scenery that can be adapted in different plays) would have been 'floated' on a simple system of grooves. Normansfield is now the only theatre in Britain where such grooves still exist – in all other theatres, the scene-changing systems and the scenery itself have long been updated or totally replaced.

Apart from its use for religious purposes, the theatre continued to be used after the war, mainly for staff dances, cabaret appearances and fund raising events organised by the League of Friends of the Hospital. In 1975, dance teacher and choreographer, Wolfgang Stange, created movement therapy workshops for the patients, later resulting in celebrated performances, which were also produced in the theatre (see Chapter 16).

The hospital grounds were also used in a number of television productions including *The Professionals*, *Our Friends In The North*, various Benny Hill shows and also a Tommy Cooper 'special' written in part by the author's father, Eric Merriman. The proximity of Thames Television at the Teddington Studios proved extremely convenient for location filming at Normansfield. More recently, scenes from an episode of *Inspector Poirot* series were filmed there. Staff from the Down's Syndrome Association who now occupy office space in the main building were left amused and a little bemused by the behaviour of actor David Suchet, who insisted on remaining 'in character' as the Belgian detective long after the filming had ceased.

In 1987, an application was made to turn the theatre and other facilities into a National Arts Centre for Disabled People. Actors Brian and Elspet (née Gray) Rix, whose daughter, Shelley, was a resident at the hospital, were active and vocal members of the League of Friends and were prime movers of the scheme. There was, however, opposition to this ambitious plan on a number of fronts. Arts bodies were not keen, some local residents were concerned about the creation of 'a ghetto for the handicapped' and many disabled people themselves understandably preferred to be integrated into mainstream arts schemes.

In the end the application was turned down by the local authority. Several years later the Rix's found themselves fronting another important campaign, this time to save the theatre from 'going dark' forever. When a decision to close the hospital was made in the mid 1980's, the very existence of the theatre was inevitably under threat. By now president of Mencap, and soon to become patron of the Langdon Down Trust, Brian Rix was very much involved in the battle to restore to glory 'one of the jewels of Victorian theatre history'. He worked very closely with the Theatres Trust which had initially become involved with the project in the early 1980's. When Normansfield and its surrounding land were to be sold for development, there was much uncertainty about what would happen to the theatre.

After complex negotiation, the Theatres Trust agreed to accept the duty of care and to set up an organisation to run the theatre. But first the developers would have to undertake substantial restoration work to the building and its precious contents. With the future of the theatre clarified, Rix was naturally delighted: "I couldn't be more thrilled," he said. "It will be restored to something quite extraordinary in the end. I think it will add enormously to the gaiety of the nation".

The restoration of the theatre (which, incidentally, is still not complete) was eventually initiated by Laing Homes, who acquired the site in 1999. It was actually a condition of the planning permission that the theatre would be conserved and reopened. The theatre is now owned and managed by the Langdon Down Centre Trust. It may not have exactly added to the 'gaiety of the nation' in the same way that Lord Rix's spiritual home, the Whitehall Theatre has done, but it has at least provided the opportunity for theatrical performances to light up again this beautiful hall.

It is quite fitting and indeed inspiring that the long tradition of the Normansfield Christmas Carol Concerts has been revived. Various groups such as Singing Hands, Twenty One and Co and the extraordinary Larondina Dance Company, formed entirely of dancers with Down's Syndrome, participate annually in the seasonal festivities.

Staff members of the Down's Syndrome Association are also following in the footsteps of their predecessors so carefully selected by Mary Langdon Down. Press officer Marie Benton is a member of the multicultural, multi-talented Many Rivers Gospel Choir, and Ruth Beckmann, an information officer at the DSA, has formed the Langdon Down Singers, who perform stunning classical choral pieces each Christmas.

Unfortunately, the excellent Strathcona Theatre Company, due to take up residency at the theatre, disbanded due to financial difficulties. The much-lamented company founded in 1982 devised original, pioneering and inspirational work and employed a number of actors with disabilities. The productions were of the highest quality, imbued with truthfulness and enthusiasm. What was always striking was that, unlike other 'inclusive' theatre groups, Strathcona was never tokenistic, and the disabled actors and actresses played a full part in productions. It is very sad that the company no longer exists and will never perform at the Normansfield theatre. After all, acting was central to the philosophy of the hospital.

John Langdon Down maintained that:

> *Care should be taken to furnish him (the patient) with varied amusements, the playground should be enlivened by music, he should be encouraged to activity in the sports as far as his physical development admits. The winter evenings should be rendered cheerful by the magic lanthorn (sic) concerts, dancing and especially theatrical representations which are not only amusing, but educational, by cultivating those faculties which have been necessarily neglected in he more practical school and industrial routine.*

With the creative use of role-play, particularly in 'shopping' lessons where pupils would act as shopkeepers or customers in order to learn the basic principles of money, weights and measures, John Langdon Down developed drama techniques that helped the residents become better integrated into society. As Francesca Byrne writes:

He was discovering for himself and his patients a style of therapy
that would pave the way for future practitioners and would enable
those with learning difficulties to benefit from a wide range of
intellectual and artistic stimulants.

The role of the theatre at Normansfield cannot be underestimated in the unfolding drama of the institution. The words from the prologue at the beginning of this chapter are not merely casual poetry but express the underlying philosophy of the Langdon Downs. Drama at the hospital was certainly not 'an aimless pleasure' – a much higher purpose was indeed the aim.

According to Peter Longman of the Theatres Trust, Britain has very few complete theatres built before 1880 and Normansfield's working stage and scenery are 'a unique document of a theatre technology now extinct.' The Normansfield theatre, unique in its quality and rarity, has remained largely intact and unaltered, and is of national importance.

Exterior of 'The Entertainment Hall'.

CHAPTER EIGHT

THE FIRST LADY

*Dr Langdon Down has been ably assisted in this work
by Mrs Langdon Down, who is pre-eminently a lady of
Miss Florence Nightingale's type, being naturally of a
sympathetic spirit, so devotedly winsome and loving in
disposition as to be looked up to by every pupil with
affection and simplicity. To our mind this is one of the great
secrets of Dr Langdon Down's success in the treatment of
his patients. Besides this, Normansfield is more like a home
than a college or an institution. It has all the comforts and
associations of a home, with the accompaniments of mental
and medical training and treatment.*

Christian Union, 27th June 1879

There is no doubt that the driving force behind John Langdon Down's Normansfield was his wife, Mary, whom he had married in a Baptist ceremony in 1860. She is described as an able, cultured woman, fluent in French and a talented pianist. The former Mary Crellin became a fearsome administrator and an astute businesswoman, who appeared to take total control in the day to day organisation of the institution. As previously explained, the hospital was run like a huge family. Apart from the nuclear element of John and Mary Langdon and, in later years, their offspring, the extended family consisted of staff and patients, who referred to Mary as 'Little Mother'.

Conor Ward writes that, at the age of 39, Mary Langdon Down took on a vast number of roles at Normansfield and acted as:

> *. . . financial director, nursing administrator, catering officer, works manager, personnel officer and public relations officer.*

101

Following the admission of a patient, she made her own notes on 'likes and dislikes', established bedtime rituals, determined fears or phobias and also carefully recorded the various illnesses such as chicken pox, whooping cough and measles borne by the patients during their hospitalisation. Beyond that, she also acquired all the furniture, ordered all the supplies and even negotiated with Hampton Court Gas Company for a reduction in gas charges.

Mary Langdon Down at work.

To say 'Little Mother' ran a tight ship is actually to play down her exacting qualities. She was quite obsessive in administrative matters and the Normansfield finances were not exempt. She was responsible for the payment and collection of fees and was meticulous in all her bookkeeping activities, recording all income and outgoing in great detail. Of course, the Langdon Downs had sunk a great deal of money into the hospital and they needed not only to recoup their investment but to turn over a profit despite significant overheads. In 1880, there were over 100 members of staff on the books, consisting of attendants, male and female servants and gardeners and labourers.

Interestingly enough, and reflecting the Langdon Downs' strong religious convictions, it was the chaplain who was the highest paid of all the staff members. And in the true Corinthian spirit of Normansfield, the Reverend Alfred Edward Beavan, who served for nearly 50 years in a full time capacity and conducted John Langdon Down's funeral, was regarded in his prime as one of the best hockey goalkeepers in England.

Staffing at Normansfield was entirely Mary Langdon Down's domain and she set out guidelines that had to be strictly observed by 'servants':

RULES TO BE OBSERVED BY THE OFFICERS OF THE ESTABLISHMENT, 1888.

The hour of rising is 6am. All servants must be properly washed and dressed and be ready to commence duty at 6.30am. The hour of leaving duty for nurses and attendants is 8pm except for those whose turn it is to take evening duty. Servants must retire to their rooms by 10.15pm, be in bed and have the gas extinguished or lowered for the night by 10.30pm. Smoking is not allowed in the house or grounds. Tobacco and pipes must be kept where pupils cannot get at them and where they will not render the house offensive. Servants are strictly forbidden to inflict seclusion or restraint or punishment of any kind upon a pupil. A fine of five shillings will be given for breaking this rule. The second offence renders the servant liable to instant dismissal. If a pupil needs any correction it must be brought to the notice of the head of department or Mrs Langdon Down.

9

DUTIES OF
SOUTH WING GOVERNESSES.

———❈———

1.—Governesses must make themselves thoroughly acquainted with the rules for officers and servants, with the names of the children and servants, and the numbers of the rooms.

2.—They must be very observant of both children and servants, and very accurate in all that concerns both, so that the servants may be treated with justice and impartiality; and that the children's inability to report anything concerning themselves may be supplemented.

3.—They should be neat and orderly themselves, and require neatness from others.

4.—They should at all times attend to the temperature and ventilation of rooms, the consumption of gas and water, and the proper care of the premises and furniture. Ventilation is to be provided from the top sashes.   Windows are never to be raised from the bottom when children are in the room.

5.—They must report any ailment of the children, however slight; chilblains, colds, bruises, scratches, &c.; also any wants of the children, or any necessary alterations in regulations, or anything amiss as to food, &c.

6.—The general neatness of children must be reviewed after breakfast and before each time of going out.   For this purpose they should pass singly before a governess. Special things to be observed : boot and shoe fastenings, dress fastenings, hair ribbons, condition of teeth, ears, eyes, hands, and nails.

Mary's duties extended far beyond maintaining staff order. John Langdon Down always felt that a balanced diet was an important part of a patient's treatment and he entrusted Mary with delivering nutritious daily fare. Happily, Mary Langdon Down's house-

Female staff 1880's.

keeping book is safely in the archive at the Langdon Down Trust
Centre. Apart from her recipes for such diverse treats as ginger
beer, panada (a traditional bread and milk dish), suckling pig and
'fruit cream ice', it also contains hints on polishing brass, cleaning
silk, knitting stockings, the treatment of boils, clarifying yeast,
preparing coffee for 30 people and poultry rearing. Conor Ward
adds:

> *Mary was also the hostess at a number of major events which*
> *required great organisation. For the opening of the new wings and*
> *the theatre in 1879, two hundred guests were entertained. The band*
> *of the Grenadier Guards were engaged to provide background*
> *music. Outside caterers were brought in and luncheon was served*
> *in the recreation hall. When the International Medical Congress*
> *was held in London in August 1881, three large receptions were*
> *held in honour of the visitors. – this time caterers were asked to*
> *prepare for eight hundred guests!*

As explained elsewhere, Mary also pursued her love of theatre in
her dynamic role as actress and manager of the Genesta Club and
she was actively involved in the shows and entertainment that took
place at Normansfield.

Apart from his work at Normansfield and continuing to work
at the London Hospital, John Langdon Down also developed a

private consulting practice, later purchasing premises in Harley Street. It's interesting to note that Mary would sometimes write to John at the Harley street address in regard to a Normansfield query:

> *Normansfield*
> *Hampton Wick*
>
> *14th March 1890*
>
> *Dearest,*
>
> *I think you had better answer the enclosed. I am glad you have such a fine day for going to the hospital. Take care of yourself and remember how precious you are to your loving wife.*
>
> *Mary*

There is also a letter written two years earlier that perhaps reveals the intimate yet somewhat formal nature of their relationship:

> *Dearest*
>
> *I am thinking that perhaps I shall come up to town this afternoon and shall sleep at Harley Street. If so I should like you to sleep there also. Send word before I come.*
>
> *Yours lovingly*
>
> *Mary*

Mary Langdon Down corresponded regularly with parents and relatives of the patients and although extremely businesslike in her manner, she also took time to assuage concerned family members as to the health and happiness of their sons, daughters, brothers or sisters.

David Hillyer, suffering from 'idiocy', was the 54th patient to be admitted to Normansfield on 5th April 1871 aged six. His home address was in Balham and his widowed mother, Ellen Hillyer, provided the consent for his admission.

On admission, David's casebook notes state:

*A diminutive child – coarse skin and oblique eyes brown. Father
dead. Mother living and healthy. Walks with a rolling gait. Fair
health – normal bodily function. All characteristics of mongolian
type of idiot. Speaks very instinctively, is a great mimic. He cannot
do anything for himself in any way. No convulsions or fits.
There is no history of imbecility in the family.*

David Hillyer in profile. From the 1912 series of photographs by Reginald Langdon Down.

John Langdon Down's original case notes on David Hillyer.

David appeared to settle in very happily for the first few weeks and entries report that he continues to improve 'in general intelligence'. His mother wrote many letters to Mary Langdon Down concerning her 'Davie', often to arrange his visits home, which he does frequently under the supervision of an attendant:

October 17th 1881

We find some difficulty with David's visit which we have not had before as the servant who used to take care of him for many years has left us, and our new servant does not feel equal to the charge. I see by rule 22 that an attendant care be supplied at the charge of a guinea a week. We should be very glad if you will send us one, if possible tomorrow and if possible we should greatly prefer having the nurse who bought him home to any other who would be a stranger to us all.

He is very well and very good but of course requires constant attention and after thinking over it, the best plan seems to be to have an attendant. Will you kindly send by her some of his kindergarten work.

In a letter dated 8th June 1882, Ellen Hillyer has heard that David is to be moved within the hospital. This is rather an emotional letter as this decision has obviously been made in response to his lack of achievement during his decade at Normansfield. She writes:

I trust the change may perhaps be advantageous to him, though my heart quails before growth in years with corresponding growth in intellect. I feel as if it were a new departure for David, and as if he were put a little further from me, though I knew and feared that it must come.

She asks how patients are occupied on this 'side' of the hospital and wishes to make sure he will continue with his kindergarten studies. She also wants to be reassured that he will still dine with the other boys and will not be alone. She signs off the letter:

With renewed most grateful thanks for all the care and kindness he has enjoyed these ten years.

It is clear that Mrs Hillyer needs constant affirmation from Mary Langdon Down that her son is well cared for and perhaps there is an element of guilt that she is no longer caring for him herself.

Thursday August 1st 1882

Ellerslie, Balham Park Rd, Balham

My dear Mrs Down

We are leaving home for a few weeks but I feel that I cannot bear to do so without hearing something about David. Will you kindly write me a few lines if possible by return of post and tell me how he is and if he is now or has been to Bognor. Anything you can tell me about him will be most thankfully appreciated.

With kindest regards
believe me
yours very sincerely
Ellen Hillyer

As Davie's birthday approaches, his mother writes to tell Mary Langdon Down that she plans to buy him a toy ship that he can play with in the pools at Bognor. She is always pleased about David's annual trip to the seaside. However, having had him at home she is troubled by his physical state:

I am distressed at observing that David's right shoulder stands out much more than his left one and I fear that I can perceive a decided curvature of the spine.

This is just one of many letters in which Mrs Hillyer fears for David's health, along with her own and that of her daughter Mary, and it seems they are often in poor health for long periods of time.

12th May 1882

Will it be convenient to you to let Mr Everett bring David over for the day next Monday? We shall be away from home for a few weeks very soon and I fear I shall not be able to come over to see him before. I will enclose a little note of the trains. You have often heard me speak of Mary's continual delicacy. I am sorry to say it seems a good deal on the increase and I do not feel quite satisfied to go on without taking a first rate medical opinion, at the same time there is little that is definite beyond general weakness in her case that I hardly know who to consult. Will you tell me if Dr Down confines himself to brain cases or if it would not be going out of his way to see her and give me his advice?

Whether Dr Down ever gave other Hillyers the benefit of his medical advice we shall never know. It is clear, however, that Mrs Hillyer did have great faith in his expertise. She also often inquires after Mary Langdon Down's cough.

In a letter dating from 18th June 1888 she expresses anxiety about David's sight, following a visit he has made home:

He seemed very cheerful and bright, but I am a little uneasy about an appearance of opacity in his left eye, and shall be very glad if the doctor will examine it and let me know his opinion about it. I hope it does not indicate any serious disease.

There is a later letter from another doctor, perhaps an eye specialist, who recommends David wears glasses, which he is to use during school hours, so his eyes don't tire when reading.

In many of Ellen Hillyer's letters she replies considerately to Mary Langdon Down's own news. In one letter she refers to the wedding of Percival Langdon Down's son, Mrs Langdon Down's grandson, which is due to take place on 22nd June 1899.

I'm glad to hear he will be moving near you dear Mrs Down, for I cannot but feel it will make a terrible blank in your home - I know enough of a mother's heart to enter into your unselfish gladness in his happiness, I know enough too to feel for the unspoken shadow of your own loneliness.

Mostly though, Ellen Hillyer reiterates how grateful she is to have such frequent accounts of her 'Davie':

It is so kind of you to tell us any particulars about him and we can quite picture his good humoured face coming along with his arm around his attendant.

On 12th May 1900, Ellen sends six badges to Normansfield. These are for David to distribute amongst his friends and to be worn to celebrate the Queen's birthday.

Blythburgh,
Polworth Road,
Streatham,
S.W.

Jan y. 9. 1902

Dear Dr Langdon-Down,

I enclose a cheque for David's Quarterly expenses, with renewed warm thanks for all the care & attention bestowed upon him. I am very glad to hear that he is keeping well, & enjoyed, as far as he could, all the Christmas festivities. We are recovering, I hope, tho' slowly in my own case, but were

The correspondence between Mrs Hillyer and the hospital seems to diminish following Mary Langdon Down's death in 1900, after which Reginald takes over some of the administrative duties. Ellen Hillyer probably missed the personal nature of Mary Langdon Down's letters after so many years. Medical entries were less frequent and informative, although we know that David lived happily at Normansfield for many years.

The casebook faithfully records:

1st March 1915

Has recently lost his mother, gained 9lbs in 12 months. Is practically blind and nearly deaf. Cheerful disposition and is a general favourite. Speech limited. Occasionally goes on drives and pays visits home. Good health.

1925

Health okay. six weeks at St Leonard's.

1926

Weight a little lower walks very slowly and with difficulty inflamed swelling on cheek subsided with treatment.

These were the last entries for David, for the following year he passed away at the age of 62 – yet another testament to the care and stimulation that he received at Normansfield and in which Mary Langdon Down played a significant part.

John and Mary Langdon Down were a formidable partnership, and enjoyed an extremely long lasting and loving relationship. According to Frances Byrne, the Langdon Down's marriage was:

> *. . . the rock on which the foundation of Normansfield was built . . . the undeniable fact is that when one looks at the life of Mary Langdon Down it is remarkable that she successfully combined the Victorian ideal of the domestic Goddess, whilst being companion and equal to her husband.*

Mary Langdon Down was certainly no Nigella Lawson but she was an extraordinary woman and her contribution to the management and philosophy of Normansfield is inestimable.

In 1900, a 'flu epidemic' struck the hospital and ten patients died of it. Mary contracted pneumonia and passed away on 5th October. She was cremated at Woking and her urn was brought to Normansfield. Her obituary appeared in *The Surrey Comet* the following day:

DEATH OF MRS LANGDON DOWN

The announcement which it is our painful duty to make of the death of Mrs Mary Langdon Down, widow of the late Dr John Langdon Down of Normansfield will be read with sincere regret throughout the neighbourhood. The deceased lady, who was 72 years of age, only returned from a month's visit to Norway on Sept 3rd and up to Thursday of last week was apparently in good health. On that day, however, she contracted a severe cold, which developed into pneumonia and although the highest medical skill was obtained, she never rallied and passed away at 11am yesterday, almost on the anniversary of her late husband's decease, which occurred on Oct 7th 1896.

Mrs Langdon Down married Dr Langdon Down in 1860 when to use the late Doctor's words, "consolidated his own happiness and success." His wife was the guiding spirit, not only in the inception of Normansfield but also in its later extensive developments.

The White House was opened in May 1868 and has since grown into one of the most gigantic institutions of its kind in the country. Its development was rapid beyond all anticipation, the buildings being enlarged no fewer than ten times between 1868 and 1891, besides the addition of two adjoining mansions and several villas. In the management of such an institution it need scarcely be said that powers of organisation and grasp of detail of a very high order were necessary and it was in the possession of these gifts that Mrs Langdon Down shone in a remarkable degree. Hers was the mastermind that directed and controlled every detail connected with the management and working of Normansfield from its very foundation up till the time of her death and which has led to its great success.

She was kind, though firm in her dealings with those in her employ and by all was held in the highest regard, while among those in her own social circle she was justly esteemed for her many amiable qualities. Normansfield has for many years figured largely in the social life of the neighbourhood but perhaps chief among all the pleasing functions that have taken place there have been the performances of the Genesta Dramatic Club which was founded mainly by the exertions of Mrs Down, and which still has its home there.

We are informed that the institution will be carried on by the two sons of the deceased, Drs Reginald and Percy Langdon Down.

CHAPTER NINE

A FAMILY CONCERN

*Mongolian imbeciles are usually the offspring of feeble,
immature or exhausted parents. Thus an imbecile of this
kind is often either the first child of young parents, the last
child of a numerous family or the only child of elderly
parents. Sometimes there is a clear history of maternal
ill-health, debility or privation. Sometimes there
is parental syphilis.*

'The Mongol In Our Midst'
Francis Crookshank (1925)

A s predicted in Mary Langdon Down's obituary, sons Reginald and Percival, who had both read medicine at Cambridge, did indeed take over the management of the hospital. There was, however, a tragic backdrop to the two brothers' inheritance of Normansfield: an awful event that had occurred nearly twenty years earlier.

Despite being the eldest of the three Langdon Down sons, Everleigh seems to have been the least favourite. According to Conor Ward, there hadn't been a huge celebration of his coming of age party, whereas Percival's 21st birthday party in 1889 was spread over two days with over a thousand guests in attendance and with 'ten thousand fairy lamps had been hung in the grounds by the Brock Company who had been responsible for the illuminations at Crystal Palace.' Reginald had also been afforded a lavish celebration.

Both Percival and Reginald were dispatched to the prestigious Harrow school, but Everleigh, who was not so academically inclined, attended Charterhouse, a less prestigious public school, although still popular amongst the middle classes. University education was not planned for Everleigh, who was groomed for a military career and became a Lieutenant in the Surrey militia. He possessed a somewhat unpredictable temper and it may well have been that his parents considered that the disciplined life of an army officer would benefit him. We shall never know. At 6am on 4th August 1883 John, Mary, and Percival Langdon Down left Normansfield to catch the boat train to France. Everleigh, aged 22, and Reginald, five years his younger, remained at the hospital. A local newspaper, *The Surrey Comet* reported the ensuing events:

Everleigh Langdon Down in Surrey Militia Uniform.

DISTRESSING FATAL OCCURRENCE AT NORMANSFIELD

After breakfast Everleigh and Reginald went into the carpenter's shop. The brothers got on quite well together, but this time had a disagreement. Reginald set about turning a piece of brass on a lathe, but Everleigh wanted to get out on the river. He exploded, snatched Reginald's brass, threw it on the floor and hit it again and again with a hammer. Reginald was understandably angry and upset and James Bradley, the senior Normansfield carpenter, tried to intervene.

Reginald kicked Everleigh in the shin. What happened next is unclear. Suddenly Everleigh fell to the floor, bleeding so severely from his groin that blood gushed through his clothes on to the shavings on the floor from a wound from a heavy paring chisel. Bradley would have seen it if thrown. It wasn't.

The bleeding was torrential and Dr Gunther was sent for urgently and arrived in half an hour. He applied a tourniquet and sent for Mr Hutchinson, the senior surgeon at the London hospital. He explored the gaping wound and discovered the femoral artery and vein were cut across as well as the abductor muscle. He tied all the cut blood vessels, closed the wound and left.

Everleigh came around from the chloroform but was very weak and no pulse could be felt at the wrist. At 5.10 pm it was stated that Everleigh was dying. A brandy enema failed to revive him and he died quickly.

An inquest was called for 6th August 1883 and the distraught parents were called back from Paris. The inquest was held in the Normansfield dining room. The jury was enlisted and heard the medical evidence. James Bradley and another carpenter, Charles Roach were called to give evidence. James Bradley stated that when Everleigh fell down he called out, "You have done for me" or under cross examination, "I am done for".

Reginald said that he was very sorry and Everleigh replied, "It's not your fault, I am to blame." And Reginald said, "I did not intend to hit him." James Bradley could not say whether the chisel had been thrust in or thrown.

The coroner Dr Diplock summed up, "There was no doubt that Everleigh's death resulted from a haemorrhage or from a blood clot to the heart caused by the haemorrhage. If the chisel had been thrown

> *by Reginald with the intention of causing injury it would have been either manslaughter or murder according to whether or not it was done in the heat of the moment". The jury deliberated for 10 minutes and returned a verdict of accidental death.*

The death notice in *The Times* read:

> *On the 4th August at Normansfield, Hampton Wick from an accident, Everleigh, eldest son of J. Langdon Down, MD, FRCP, of 81 Harley Street, aged 22 years.*

The first medic at the horrific scene, Dr Gunther, a colleague and friend of the family, had not informed the police and no statement had been taken from either Everleigh or Reginald. The inquest proceedings were held in the rarefied atmosphere of Normansfield, the actual home of the victim and perpetrator and there can be little doubt that the jury would have been somewhat influenced by the family's presence.

It also extraordinary that the police were not involved straight away, even if Dr Gunther's rationale was that he didn't think that the injury would prove fatal. Reginald must have been distraught by his brother's death and to punish him further would not have contributed much to the cause of British justice, but the fact that the Langdon Downs were a distinguished and prominent medical family may have influenced such an outcome. One can only imagine the uproar if it had been a resident or another member of staff who had been involved in a similar incident. It is telling that there is no archival material available – all family correspondence from that period was apparently destroyed.

Everleigh was buried in Reigate cemetery beside his younger sister Lilian. Mary and John Langdon Down had now lost their first born son as well as their only daughter. In 1895 Reginald married Jane Cleveland, who had been a nursing sister at the London Hospital and later became involved in the running of the hospital. They had a son, John, and two daughters: Stella (who later became Lady Brain) and Elspie. When Jane Langdon Down died in 1917 Percival's wife, Helen, also known as 'Mouche', daughter of local MP James Bigwood, contributed to the day to day management at Normansfield. (Percival's daughter, Molly, also became a psychiatrist and then worked in the hospital for ten years.) Reginald remarried in 1922 and his second wife, Ruth Turnbull, bore him another son, Tony, who spent the first years of his life at Normansfield. In the ensuing years, he became a staunch supporter of the League of Friends.

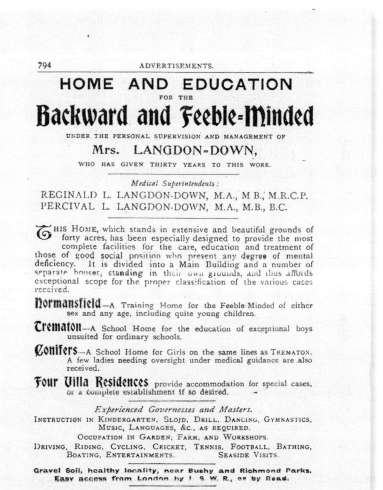

794   ADVERTISEMENTS.

HOME AND EDUCATION

FOR THE

Backward and Feeble=Minded

UNDER THE PERSONAL SUPERVISION AND MANAGEMENT OF

Mrs. LANGDON=DOWN,

WHO HAS GIVEN THIRTY YEARS TO THIS WORK.

Medical Superintendents :

REGINALD L. LANGDON-DOWN, M.A., M B., M.R.C.P.
PERCIVAL L. LANGDON-DOWN, M.A., M.B., B.C.

THIS HOME, which stands in extensive and beautiful grounds of forty acres, has been especially designed to provide the most complete facilities for the care, education and treatment of those of good social position who present any degree of mental deficiency. It is divided into a Main Building and a number of separate houses, standing in their own grounds, and thus affords exceptional scope for the proper classification of the various cases received.

Normansfield—A Training Home for the Feeble-Minded of either sex and any age, including quite young children.

Crematon—A School Home for the education of exceptional boys unsuited for ordinary schools.

Conifers—A School Home for Girls on the same lines as TREMATON. A few ladies needing oversight under medical guidance are also received.

Four Villa Residences provide accommodation for special cases, or a complete establishment if so desired.

Experienced Governesses and Masters.

INSTRUCTION IN KINDERGARTEN, SLOJD, DRILL, DANCING, GYMNASTICS, MUSIC, LANGUAGES, &C., AS REQUIRED.

OCCUPATION IN GARDEN, FARM, AND WORKSHOPS.

DRIVING, RIDING, CYCLING, CRICKET, TENNIS, FOOTBALL, BATHING, BOATING, ENTERTAINMENTS.   SEASIDE VISITS.

Gravel Soil, healthy locality, near Bushy and Richmond Parks. Easy access from London by L. S. W. R., or by Road.

For Terms and Particulars address :—

NORMANSFIELD, HAMPTON WICK.

119

It is a remarkable coincidence that John Langdon Down's first grandson, named after his illustrious grandfather, born to Reginald and Jane in 1905, had 'Mongolism'. Jane apparently never came to terms with this fact and was described by Tony Langdon Down as very highly strung:

John Langdon Down named after his celebrated grandfather.

She made the great mistake of trying to insist there was nothing wrong with John. He was at first sent to an ordinary school, but it didn't work and he was very unhappy. It was only when she died it was accepted that he couldn't possibly live a normal life. He listened to lots of music, was never seen without a book and he used to play snooker. He lived with a splendid carer called Amy in part of the main centre, so I got to know him very well and was very fond of him. He was in many ways extremely intelligent though he lacked the ability to look after himself.

When the family eventually moved out of Normansfield, John moved into the North Wing where he had his own room and by all accounts he was very popular and led a very happy life. John remained at the hospital until his death in 1971 at the age of 65. There are a number of pictures of him as a child taken by Reginald who was a very keen photographer. Curiously there are none of John in adulthood available in the archives.

Reginald's daughter, Elspie (later Elspie Cusden), lived at Normansfield between 1904 and 1916. Her experience was similar to her siblings John and Stella in that Normansfield was the family home and they all resided in the main building. Each room had a number and every person whether staff, patient or Langdon Down family member, occupied their rooms in consecutive order with no distinction as to hospital hierarchy. She explained:

Our rooms were numbered in sequence with those of the North and South wings on either side of us. The room my sister and I shared was 102 and our family sitting room was 86. I never looked at them as numbers, but considered them names. I like to think that having a family living in the centre of such an institution was bound to make for a general family feeling for we really did try to make it more of a home than an institution. Every member of the "Normansfield family" was viewed as just as important as his fellows.

Not every member of staff was happy with this arrangement, however, for the 1899 staff record book shows the linen keeper resigned her position as she objected to taking her meals with the patients.

Elspie recalled her childhood in the hospital with much fondness:

> *We could hear much that went on either side of us and in some*
> *rooms above us, but we took little notice of this and although some*
> *outsiders may have thought it a bad place in which to bring up*
> *children, I do not feel this, for the atmosphere throughout the whole*
> *institution was happy not sad.*

As part of a pioneering occupational therapy programme, Elspie
set up several looms and taught weaving to some of the girls,
particularly those from Conifers who were more disabled. She also
supervised the manufacture of a number of carpets and in time,
more looms were bought for the farm buildings where linen and
woollens were produced.

Tony Langdon Down was actually born at Normansfield in
December 1922 and lived there until he was nine. For the first
few years he was looked after by an elderly Scottish nanny. In an
interview with Heather Cadbury, Tony recalled that he didn't see
that much of his ageing parents, but that they were very loving and
that he also looked back at his childhood with great happiness:

> *We had the use of what was really a lovely garden and tennis courts*
> *and I vividly remember Sunday tennis parties. The accommodation*
> *was very grand. The dining and drawing rooms were very beautiful*
> *rooms and it was all very comfortable. We had children's parties in*
> *the theatre, and there used to be an annual show for the residents.*
> *On those occasions my father (Reginald Langdon Down) used to*
> *present watches and clocks to all of the staff who had been there for*
> *twenty one years. Some indeed stayed on for fifty years!*

Tony became great friends with many of the senior staff, a lot of
whom were artisans employed in the workshops at Normansfield.
These included an upholsterer, an electrician, painters, carpenters and
a plumber, Herbert Smith, who taught the six year old Tony how
to box. It was also quite useful to have skilled artisans 'on site' as
any work that was required in the Langdon Down living quarters
was done by them. There was a laundry down near Trematon where
all the washing was done, which came in particularly handy in later
years when Tony took up boating and needed his sails washed.

JLD's grandson seems unwilling to lend a hand!

Up until just after the end of the Second World War, the Normansfield farm played a huge part in the running of the institution. Tony Langdon Down evoked fond memories of the homestead:

> One of the attractions for a small boy was the fact that roughly forty acres were actively farmed and there was a herd of about three hundred pigs, a herd of various, rather unusual cattle, Dexters and Kerries in particular, which provided all the milk for the residents. Trematon was where the higher grade men lived and it was mostly those that worked on the farm.

All the pork and eggs came from the farm and at different times there were over a 100 chickens, 50 turkeys plus an elegant dovecote of white fantail pigeons. The various animals were naturally of great interest to the children who passed a lot of their time helping to feed them. The children were also occupied playing on the swings in the sandpit in one of the large playing fields and there were also 'competitive, simple games' where packets of sweets were offered as prizes.

Eventually, Reginald and his wife decided it would be better if the family didn't actually live on the premises. In the early 1930's

Family portraits of John Langdon Down's two sons: above, Percival and below, Reginald seen here with his son, John, himself having Down's syndrome.

Reginald Langdon Down received permission to live away from the hospital whilst performing his role as the Medical Officer and subsequently bought a house in nearby Broom Road.

Percival Langdon Down was less career-minded than his brother and has been described as 'a people's person' whose strength was the daily care of the patients. He died aged 58 in 1925 and his obituary in *The Surrey Comet* described him as, 'a gifted, earnest, self sacrificing man whose services to others would be difficult to overestimate'. The following year, Normansfield became a limited company with Reginald Langdon Down and Helen (Mouche) Langdon Down, Percival's widow, as the company's directors. As well as running Normansfield, Reginald also operated a private practice in Harley Street. Throughout the ensuing generations of the Langdon Down dynasty the institution of the family influenced the manner in which the hospital was run and thus had major considerations for the staff.

As established by John Langdon Down, each house was still organised as a family unit. Each nurse had a group of patients in her charge. This group consisted of six patients ranging in age from a few months old to the quite elderly and each nurse was held fully responsible for her patients' welfare, clothes and health. From 1900 to 1914 Normansfield was divided into four areas. There was one wing for women and children, another for men and boys, and two houses: one for 'higher grade' women and one for 'higher grade' men. Each of these groups had their own area of the garden and parkland within the hospital grounds.

A kindergarten with several teachers provided education and every August the hospital moved en-masse for six weeks to a large boarding school in Worthing that was rented during the school holidays. Preparations for the holiday were frenetic: a specially commissioned train conveyed the household along with the bedding, linen, crockery and trunks of clothing, not to mention the commodes and wheelchairs. The Worthing school was set in beautiful grounds, a 100 yards from the sea with its own private path to the beach. Patients went for walks along the sea front in the mornings and then to the beach in the afternoons for 'paddling'. In later years, between the wars, there were weekly coach trips to local beauty spots, which was described by staff and patients as 'the highlight of the year' and anticipated with great enthusiasm.

It is possible to gain an insight into conditions for those working at the hospital from the testimony of ones who served. In 1934 a nurse Hall joined Normansfield as a resident assistant nurse. She worked 60 hours a week and was paid £4/8s a month. Miss Hall was given a half day off a week and on alternate Sundays either the morning or afternoon off. Staff were also allowed one full day off per month, but these days were often saved towards annual holidays. No standard uniform was supplied, instead:

> *We were given twelve yards of dress material and twelve yards*
> *of apron material and either had to pay the sewing mistress ten*
> *shillings to make them up or do them ourselves. A sewing machine*
> *was placed at our disposal if we wished to do the latter. The only*
> *thing we received ready made were our caps.*

At this time, Normansfield had 300 patients. The 'higher grade' males and females lived either at Conifers or Trematon, whilst the more difficult patients were housed in the North and South Wings of the main building. In those days, there were no wards – only a large number of well-fitted rooms where each nurse slept with her patients. One extra large room in each house served as a sick room, but even here each nurse cared for her own patients under the supervision of one partly trained officer.

Nurse Hall explained the nursing system in a 1992 interview:

> *Whilst off duty, another nurse was given charge of the group and*
> *you, in turn, took charge of hers whilst she was off duty. This*
> *meant that the children had a wonderful sense of security because*
> *they had the same nurse at all times.*

In case of serious illness, nurse Hall recalled:

> *Dr Reginald or his son-in-law, Lord Brain, were on call day or*
> *night. One non-resident assistant nurse acted as night nurse in each*
> *house. This might sound like something out of Dickens but not so,*
> *the patients were cared for not as a crowd but as individuals.*

She was also extremely impressed by the quality of nursing care and the supervision given by the top brass:

A strict check was made each week by both our chief officer and Mrs Percival Langdon Down. These checks were made at random which meant that all staff were kept on their toes. None of our officers were medically trained but all were great organisers and had a deep understanding of the needs of the handicapped child. Especially our chief officer, Miss Cleke, who served at Normansfield for 50 years. She handled her staff in a masterful way and had an eagle eye for anything that was not right. All staff could go to her with any problem, either personal or work-wise and however difficult the obstacle, Miss Cleke always found the right solution. Her staff adored her even though there were times when they trembled at her wrath if wrong doing had taken place.

THE TAMESIS CLUB

Following John Langdon Down's extension of the Normansfield grounds to the River Thames, he had also a Boathouse built (1884) and the resulting access to the river thus made it possible for a number of visitors to arrive by boat.

The Tamesis club was established in 1885 as a spin off from the Thames sailing club at Surbiton. The sailors' first clubhouse was at Alfred Burgoine's Boathouse at Hampton Wick, just downstream of Kingston Bridge. John Langdon Down became one of the first Presidents of Tamesis, which may indicate he was a generous contributor to the clubhouse at Burgoine's.

The Langdon Down family maintained strong links with this local sailing club; Reginald and Percival became keen sailors (they owned a 'Surbiton gig' called 'Catseye') and were among the club's first members. They were certainly enthusiastic, but it seems not always the most adept according to this Tamesis regatta report:

'Catseye, last, was the only one to set her spinnaker and, unfortunately, got it overboard in taking it in, losing as much ground as she gained it. She could not save her time, although most pluckily sailed throughout the match.'

Despite this nautical mishap, Percival was later to become commodore of the club between 1922 and 1925 and Norman Langdon Down held the same prestigious position between 1958 and 1964. Norman's wife Patricia, son James and daughter Martha sailed with Tamesis for many years. Tony Langdon Down also recalled, 'All the family had boats and ours was a Merlin Ricket – a fourteen foot sailing dinghy'.

Tamesis Sailing Club played a significant role in the development of dinghy racing on the River Thames in the nineteenth century and today remains a thriving organisation.

It seemed that Reginald, like his mother, was also rather talented in selecting suitable staff and would actually engage untrained but 'kindly' nurses, who he felt were more suited to the work at Normansfield. He actually promoted a Trematon housemaid to be the house matron at the house – a position she subsequently held for many years.

Despite the long hours and extremely demanding work, nurse Hall described her working environment as very happy. She felt the family system provided unique personal contact and was a significant reason why a number of staff stayed on for so many years at Normansfield.

Wintertime at Normansfield: seasonal postcards were sent out and staff enjoy skating on the Thames in front of the boathouse.

There was no doubt that many of the staff enjoyed the wider Normansfield experience. As nurse Hall explained:

> We also had lots of fun. Dances in the main hall every Monday afternoon, a cinema show every Wednesday and each house held a party on the birthday of every child. Many of our nurses were extremely clever with their hands and each day classes were held to teach the children such crafts as weaving, sewing, knitting, painting and bead work. We also had a part-time teacher of physical exercises. She came each day to give the patients a varied regime of drill and also taught the higher grade children Old Time dancing.

As in previous generations, the contemporary crop of Langdon Downs continued to celebrate Christmas with great enthusiasm. Preparations began several weeks in advance. Reginald and Elspie would peruse the warehouse of a local department store in order to choose presents for the patients. Patients knew that the seasonal festivities were well and truly on their way when a magnificently sized Christmas tree was placed centre stage in the theatre.

The staff made all their own decorations and each house was in competition to produce the most exceptional ornamentation. A church service was held in the main hall on Christmas morning at which all the patients attended. According to nurse Hall, they participated in the carol singing 'with great gusto'. There then followed a table-creaking Christmas lunch complete with wine and afterwards all the Langdon Down family emerged to give the patients their gifts from the Christmas tree. Nurse Hall observed:

> Most of our patients came from well-to-do families and many and varied were the gifts. The rest of the day was spent by the children playing with their toys whilst the exhausted staff endeavoured to draw fresh breath.

Another festive highlight took place early in the new year when the staff and more able patients paid an annual visit to the pantomime at Drury Lane Theatre. The residents donned full evening dress while staff went in uniform. The party travelled up to Covent Garden by coach and were always seated in the front row of the dress circle.

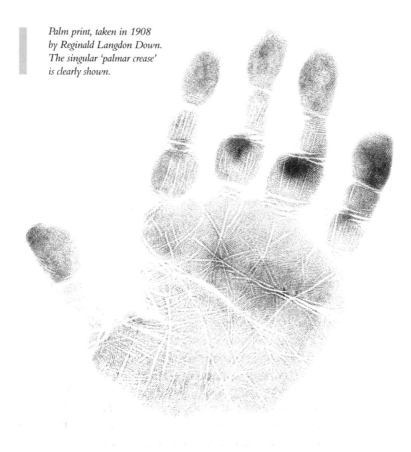

Palm print, taken in 1908 by Reginald Langdon Down. The singular 'palmar crease' is clearly shown.

In terms of medical research at Normansfield, John Langdon Down had obviously been the major force, but his son, Reginald, continued his father's work. Reginald's contribution to the various 'stigmata' that define Down's syndrome was to identify what is now referred to as the 'singular palmar or simian crease'.

In 1909, he exhibited the handprints of a number of patients with Down's syndrome indicating that:

> *The bones of the palm differed from the normal in their extreme irregularity, and the tendency of the principal fold-lines to be two in number only, instead of three was the most commonly the case.*

This observation is still used as one of the methods to distinguish Down's syndrome in newborn babies.

There was one area, however, in which Reginald did not excel himself as described by Conor Ward:

> *Speaking at a meeting of the Medico-Psychological Society, Reginald stated that the "Mongolian" abnormality must be a "reversion to a type even further back than the Mongol stock, from which some ethnologists believe all the various races of men have sprung".*

Francis Crookshank, a London physician whose book, the delightfully titled, *A Mongol in Our Midst*, theorised that, 'Mongolian imbecility represented regression to the characteristics of the Orang Utan', later referred to this statement. Crookshank held that children with features of 'primitive races were not fully developed in the womb and were more like primates, who preceded even the inferior Mongol race'. As if lunatics, idiots and imbeciles were not sufficiently gruesome descriptions, children and people with what we know now as Down's syndrome were now likened to being the elusive 'missing links'.

In fact it was Darwin's theory of 'survival of the fittest' that led his cousin Sir Francis Galton to applying Darwin's theory to ethnicity in humans. In *The Politics Of Mental Handicap*, Joanna Ryan writes that it was 1869 when Galton coined the term 'eugenics' for the first time and then described that its purpose was, 'to produce a highly gifted race of men by judicious marriages during several consecutive generations'.

Its beliefs directly influenced the Aryan race theory of the Nazis. Galton defined two types of eugenics: 'positive eugenics' was the preferential breeding of superior individuals in order to improve the genetic stock of the human race; 'negative eugenics' was the discouragement or prohibition of reproduction by individuals thought to have inferior genes. This was to be achieved by counselling or sterilisation – voluntary or enforced. Francis Galton also founded the Eugenics Society in 1907 (known as the Eugenics Education Society until 1926) in order to expand eugenic teaching. Supporters of the British Eugenics Society were quite a mixed bag. Winston Churchill MP was a supporter as were Sidney and Beatrice Webb, founders of the Labour Party, and many other influential intellectuals of the left and right. As Home Secretary at the time of the Mental Deficiency Act of 1913, Winston Churchill was reported in Hansard as saying:

> *The unnatural and increasingly rapid growth of the feebleminded classes, coupled with a steady restriction among all the thrifty, energetic and superior stocks, constitutes a race danger. I feel that the source from which the stream of madness is fed should be cut off and sealed up before another year has passed.*

Interestingly, Reginald Langdon Down was Vice President of the Eugenics Society between 1909 and 1911, just a few years after the birth of his 'Mongoloid' son, John. He subsequently became director of the society in 1936 and was a supporter, in some cases, of the sterilisation of women with learning disabilities. Dr Carlos Paton Blacker, who was General and then Honorary Secretary for a period of 30 years between 1931 and 1961 whilst Reginald was Director, investigated atrocities committed by Nazi doctors and commented that although none of the experiments produced scientific conclusions and though the methods used by the Nazis were unfortunate, euthanasia of the insane was 'acceptable'.

There was another relative of the Langdon Downs who had been member of the Eugenics Society in the mid 1950's and made front page newspaper headlines a quarter of a century later. Dr Leonard Arthur (Stella Brain's son-in-law) was charged with the attempted murder of John Pearson, described then as 'a new-born mongol baby.'

John Pearson, who was born on 28th June 1980 at the Derbyshire City Hospital, was rejected soon after his birth by his mother who told her husband she did not want to keep him. The highly respected consultant paediatrician Dr Arthur allegedly wrote in the notes:

> *Parents do not want the child to survive. Nursing care only.*

John Pearson was prescribed a sedative and water, but no food, and died from 'Bronchopneumonia, as a result of Down's syndrome' just over two days after his birth. Dr Arthur did not give evidence on his own behalf at his trial, but a huge number of medical colleagues provided supportive evidence. One of them was Sir

Douglas Black who was the current President of the Royal College of Physicians. Justice Farquarson, the trial judge, described him to the jury as a man 'at the pinnacle of his profession' and repeated to the jury the evidence given by Sir Douglas, including this damning passage:

> *I say that it is ethical, in the case of a child suffering from Down's, and with a parental wish that it should not survive, to terminate life providing other considerations are taken into account such as the status and ability of the parents to cope in a way that the child could otherwise have had a happy life.*

Dr Arthur had been initially charged with murder, but questions about the child suffering from possible congenital heart failure caused the original charge to be altered to 'attempted murder'. Dr Arthur's defence, led by distinguished QC, George Carmen, was that he had allowed the baby to die as humanely as possible by deciding not to treat his pneumonia.

Mr Carmen used Biblical references to justify Arthur's actions and told the jury:

> *He could, like Pontius Pilate, have washed his hands of the matter. He did not, because good doctors do not turn away. Are we to condemn him as a criminal because he helped two people at the time of their greatest need? Are we to condemn a doctor because he cared?*

Dr Arthur was cleared of the charge by the jury at Leicester Crown Court on 5th November 1981 on the grounds that he had not committed the act of 'positive euthanasia' . . . he had merely let nature take its course.

George Carmen later described this acquittal as his finest hour.

CHAPTER TEN

AN OCCASIONAL RUMPUS

Civilisation . . . is the acceptance and
the encouragement of differences.

Mahatma Gandhi (1869-1948)

Annie Campbell was a cleaner at Normansfield for a short period before the Second World War. Her son, Colin, was treasurer of the Teddington Reminiscence Group for many years and Annie was interviewed in 1993 by Susan New. I am grateful to Heather Cadbury for allowing reproduction of the interview in full.

'I was born in Teddington, on the 5th of July 1901, the Annies Cottages, Clifton Road. It runs into Church Road. My mother's name was Annie, and nearly everyone I knew, the women, were Annies. But I was never known as Annie. Something I was supposed to have said as a small child stuck and I just became Duke. No one in the family ever calls me anything else.

I think it was somehow to do with the fact that my mother was Annie, my cousin's daughter was Annie, there were so many Annies that they just left me with a pet name. It was "Doog", I made it "Duke" because it looks so horrible to sign Doog. I suddenly started making it Duke. Later I asked my mother, when I was about ten, why they called me Duke and she said, "Well we couldn't call you a Duchess, so we called you Duke."

I went to work at Normansfield just before the Second World War, 1938. In my late thirties. I couldn't get a job at that stage and I wanted work in tailoring. Any job was good enough so I tried Normansfield. I saw an advert for cleaning and general assistance. It must have been in one of the local papers.'

So you thought you would go for that, even though you were a tailor?

'Well you see I wasn't entitled to unemployment money. They asked me for an interview, and I went. The matron of the house of Trematon, she must have liked the look of me because I told her I had never done this work before, but I had cleaned my own home and I assumed it would be similar, and she said, "Well I think you will be all right, in time." So I started and at the end of the fortnight she said to me "Oh you have improved you know, you have got so much quicker!" But you see it was run on hospital grounds and I had never had anything much to do with hospitals.'

It's a different skill isn't it, cleaning on a professional level. What are the differences compared with cleaning your own place?

'They were bigger rooms, quite a lot bigger, several beds in each dormitory. It was a very nice, big house. There were a number of them very similar. In the grounds at the back of the main hospital building. It was very nice piece of ground at the back.

At first I was a bit in awe, I think, because I didn't know what sort of inmates there might be. I found if you smiled at them and talked to them, they asked you questions. Some of them were very sensible, I didn't think they should be there. But I never fell out with anyone there. I met them really in the dining room, they had a beautiful table and the food was extremely good.

They had a matron who supervised the whole place, and there were one or two inside staff. I got very friendly with one of the women, one of the housemaids. They had what we used to call as kids their keepers. Well as a small child we used to see them in crocodile fashion, the better grade ones going to the pictures at Teddington, the Savoy.

They walked from Hampton Wick you see. That was when I was quite young, I can't remember a time when we didn't know Normansfield house. The tough ones were in the other buildings.

The more mentally retarded ones were not in the house I was in. I didn't really meet them. We used to see them in the grounds. I remember one who used to walk around with a barrow upside down. They were all private (patients).

We used to have a mid morning breakfast. It was a lunch I suppose and we all met round a kitchen table. There was quite a crowd of us and on one occasion we were joking together and I said, "You are much better up top than I thought you were when I was younger."

The men who looked after the inmates would be there and the indoor staff. They were all men where I was. One man used to stand in the hallway and as one walked up the stairs occasionally he would touch your leg. So I used to walk backwards upstairs. I told my friend Edith about him and she said, "Tread on his fingers. He won't do it to you any more!" She also said, "He is a titled man. He should be quite somebody, but he is mentally unfit!"

Did you feel a bit sort of vulnerable?

'Odd thing, I never did. I wasn't there for very long because I had a problem health-wise. I was there long enough to realise how good it was. They had two schoolmasters. They took me over the school rooms and also showed me the farm. They had a farm. One thing that stands out in my memory is the beautiful colour of the pigs. They got three pigs - boars that they were going to put on show and they were scrubbed to a beautiful pink colour.

I remember, in the school, the older man used to instruct the ones who could do anything sensible and also I remember one man that was absolutely an idiot to look at. He sat in a corner with a very big box and a bale of wool that he teased into wool, which could be used for knitting. I said, "That's a boring job," to the school master. He said, "He loves it and he does it beautifully, nobody helps him. So we leave him while he is happy." Do you know they made, for the new church in Hampton Wick St Marks, all the altar clothes? They were beautiful. Materials like linen, they were scarlet and beautifully white. It is amazing what those people can do with patience and understanding by the persons who taught them. School was a glorified shed really, out-houses.

We never saw the children, except when they were put out in prams or pushchairs in the sunshine. Well I saw a baby that didn't

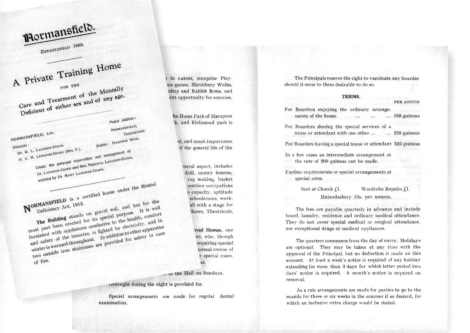

look many months old and its features was of an absolute idiot. I would imagine they went to a nursery type place, you see there were a lot of houses there and I only saw one.'

How did they deal with people who were difficult?

'Well, I think the men who looked after them would hold them down. But I don't know for sure. There was one inmate that seemed to have a fit or something came over him every few weeks and several times while I was there he used to go into the washroom and kick a basin and he always hurt his toe. Occasionally he cracked a basin.

There was a young fellow partly coloured [on the staff]. He was a very clever young fellow, his mother was a matron of a hospital and she had a lot to do with mental cases and he told me he was brought up with it.

He was a doctor's son, but his mother made the mistake of having him by the doctor and he was a married man. I assume the doctor was Asian. He was a nice fellow, but he was so hurt because he couldn't get into the army. It was only because of his colour. He was quite young I should think, around eighteen or nineteen, and the inmates all got on well with him. He would go out and play ball with them. His mother ran a Nursing Home of her own.

I cleaned some of the bedrooms and the stairs and all that sort of thing. You used brushes, polish more than anything. Many of them had carpets and you had a long broom with a carpet brush. It was like an ordinary broom with stiff bristles. People don't realise quite how hard it was. The tea leaves used to be saved and damped and spread over the carpet to stop the dust rising. You just damp them not wetting them and just sprinkle them like sawdust over the carpet, and then brushed it. The dust stuck to the tea leaves and so that stopped it rising. It didn't stain the carpet.

There were beautiful fenders all made of brass, they all had to be polished every so often. It got a going over once a week but for spring cleaning it was extra specially cleaned. The walls were swept, the curtains came down and were cleaned and the fireplace was burnished and they had the chimney sweep.

You had soda and you had very good furniture polish that was made of beeswax, I think it was beeswax and turpentine. Plenty of soaps. The matron said to me one day "You are not a bit extravagant are you?"

I said, "I was brought up not to waste!" She said, "The other women use so much more than you do!"

There were three cleaners to my knowledge. Well I was only really part time... but it was a long part time. I went at half past eight and I came home about half past three. At that time I think I was living with my cousin Jean in Twickenham and cycled to work. It wasn't a long day such as I would have done at tailoring. It was six days a week. I was paid £1/18 shillings and had a meal. I was happy there. It's the staff that make the pleasantry. Rent was twelve shillings, usually it worked out at a third of the man's wages. I worked there about eighteen months, it wasn't very long. I left because of my health, I finished up in hospital, war broke out and I couldn't go to work. I was attending a hospital in London and when war was imminent they cleared all the patients in London down into the suburbs. My own doctor (Dr Morgan) was called up because he was a reservist. The day war broke out I was ill and his partner came to see me and while he was sitting on the edge of my bed, the matron went off to tell everyone we were at war. We knew then that war was declared. You see, I had been through the 1914 war.'

Is there anything else you would like to tell me about Normansfield?

'There was somebody who I didn't think should have been there. One chap, they made him a workshop in the loft and he used to make violins. I often wonder if he was just childish and he came from good class people. I think in those days the families just didn't want to know.

The cheapest fee there was six guineas a week and they provided all their own clothing. If they spoiled their own clothes the relatives or whoever paid for them, had to buy them. Their sheets on the bed they bought themselves. There was one bed allotted in the big room for the man who looked after them at night, there could have been possibly five or six beds in some of the big rooms.

Occasionally there would be a rumpus, but I would only hear it because the keepers, or whatever you care to call them, would all gather together if they heard noises. Whoever was nearest would go and sort it out. One fellow was there through being ragged by his fellow students. He didn't pass an examination for matriculation. He was so ragged he just went mentally wrong.'

I guess the matron would be pretty important?

'Well she certainly had no side that way. I did a bit of sewing for her once or twice and she seemed like an ordinary person to me. There were no nurses that I knew. These men were trained. In other houses where they were perhaps less able to look after themselves they might have had some nurses. It was a secretive place in a sense, because you found out very little about the inmates and I never saw any of them that had a visitor. Whether they had visitors and they were taken into the big reception room and the door was closed, I don't know.'

CHAPTER ELEVEN

NORMANSFIELD AT WAR

The demand that defective people be prevented from propagating equally defective offspring is a demand of clearest reason and, if systematically executed, represents the most humane act of mankind. It will spare millions of unfortunates' undeserved sufferings, and consequently will lead to a rising improvement of health as a whole.

'Mein Kampf'
Adolf Hitler (1924)

In 1934, the German Government passed legislation sanctioning the compulsory sterilisation of the congenitally feeble minded. Within a few years, over 400,000 Germans were sterilised – about one in every 100 of its population. This, of course, was just the beginning. Between 1939 and 1945 the Nazis carried out a euthanasia programme in which over 200,000 mentally ill, mentally handicapped and physically disabled people and over 6,000 children were killed. Described as life 'unworthy of life', they were systematically incarcerated, segregated and then killed by various means – but usually simply by starvation.

By the time war in Europe was looming, it was clear that the majority of asylums in Britain had obviously failed in their attempts at being 'therapeutic' to patients. Although there had been some hope that hospitalisation might be a temporary measure with the possibility of 'treatment' and then a return to their families, there now existed a huge number of large asylums full of long-stay patients with little or no hope of rehabilitation.

Some, classified as 'moral imbeciles', were locked away in long stay hospitals, sometimes for the rest of their lives. Many women were placed in hospitals purely on the grounds of giving birth to illegitimate children. The degeneracy of the 'lower orders' was blamed for the numbers of 'moral defectives'. E R Johnstone, president of the American Association of Mental Deficiency at the turn of the 20th century called for 'institutional care as a method of elimination' for those who showed 'arrested or incomplete development of the mind'.

There was also the belief that disabled people were highly promiscuous; women classified as feeble minded were preposterously seen as 'slaves to their animal passions' and the main strategy to curb the fertility of disabled people was to segregate them. Disabled people were represented as helpless, threatening or insane and 'reproduction of the unfit' was thought to be one of the main causes of poverty, unemployment, criminality, alcoholism and idleness. The Eugenic solution, as mentioned elsewhere, was to prevent disabled people from reproducing.

My mother-in-law, Ursula Wellemin, fled Nazi Germany as a Jewish refugee in June 1939. She had grown up in the shadows of Sonnenstein, near Dresden, a former medieval castle which was used as a mental institution and where 14,000 'mentally retarded' people were cremated and gassed.

I cannot help but ponder what might have happened had my own daughter, Sarah, been born in Germany during that period. As a 'mental defective', would she have been part of the children's euthanasia programme, or would she have survived this only to become another Jewish victim of 'The Final Solution'?

Following the outbreak of the Second World War in 1939, disruption to the usual smooth running of Normansfield was almost immediate, When war was announced on 3rd September, some of the patients were on holiday at Selsey Bill and they all had to return home after a fortnight rather than the customary six weeks.

Incredibly, there was also 'a devilish plan' during the Blitz to trick the Luftwaffe into thinking that Normansfield was actually in the heart of the capital. By lighting 'decoy' bonfires around the hospital site, the Ministry of Defence apparently thought the area, being so close to the river, would look like the centre of London from the sky and would draw the attention of German bombers! Whether the result of this MOD contrivance or the fact that the hospital was also in close proximity to the strategically vital National Physical Laboratory, local air raids were heavy and a number of bombs did actually fall on the hospital grounds.

On one Sunday in June 1944 a large bomb fell near the Conifers building, killing one patient and rendering the building uninhabitable. Every window in the hospital was shattered by the explosion and for months staff and patients lived behind boarded-up windows until repairs could be made. The grounds were hit by several V1 and incendiary bombs this time without casualties.

All the patients and staff were moved into heavily sandbagged rooms in the basement where they lived in very crowded conditions. Prior to the war, meals had always been of a very high standard, but now food rationing caused obvious problems. Every member of the staff did fire-watching duties one night a week, patrolling the grounds and roofs on a four-hour rota. Air raid shelters had been built in preparation but proved unsafe and the patients were moved to dormitories in basements in the North and South Wings. Bunks were also put up in the basement corridors.

Nurse Prentice started to work at Normansfield in July 1942 and in an interview with Heather Cadbury in 1994 recalled her initial days at the hospital very clearly:

> *They made the basement so that the residents took their mattresses down so that they could sleep down there. All this area was bombed because they were trying for the Lab (National Physical Laboratory) where Barnes Wallace was developing his bouncing bomb. They did catch the weir one night and all the water went down to the sea. The planes used to come across to the coast and up the Thames, that's how we got bombed, you see. They just followed the Thames up to London.*

Nurse Prentice spoke of a boy who seemed to know when the planes were coming. He would find his nurse, put his head under her apron, thus serving as an early air raid warning for the staff and patients:

> *Thanks to him, we always knew when the bombers were near.*

Nurse Prentice went on to describe the lay out of the hospital:

> There was the main building, in which the doctors lived. They were
> both Harley Street specialists. I worked at the South Wing and we
> had between ninety and a hundred in the South Wing. In the North
> Wing there weren't quite so many, round about sixty males and then
> in the grounds there was Conifers and Trematon. Along the main
> Kingston Road there were two houses, with private patients in.
> Also in Broom Road, which runs the other side of Normansfield by
> the river, there was a house with private patients in. In Trematon
> and Conifers there was roughly between forty and fifty. The private
> patients had their own house, their own staff but came under
> Normansfield. They were adults who were mentally deficient.
> Many of the children in Normansfield came from wealthy families
> and well known families, therefore you had to keep counsel.

The farm remained in operation until about 1943 and apart from
all the other animals that Normansfield housed, there were horses
which the staff and some patients rode out.

The farm in winter.

Tony Langdon Down recalled events at the farm during the war:

> *The farm was still going until the beginning of the war, and
> I suppose that was the time when it really wasn't possible to
> continue to look after such large numbers of animals. But the place
> was still kept in order and there was a splendid head gardener called
> Dymoth, who lived in one of the villas and who ran the whole
> place for very many years. It was no longer possible to use your own
> milk. I should add also my father, perhaps rather unhappily, started
> up the first battery chickens. He always had a great interest in new
> ideas and indeed I suppose it was quite successful in those days, but
> not something I personally think should be pursued!*

In her interview with Heather Cadbury nurse Prentice explained
working practices during the early days of the war:

> *Originally we worked sixty four hours, but it did go down to fifty
> eight, which it stayed for many years. We had one day off a month.
> We were paid two pounds with ten pence taken out for insurance,
> so it was nineteen shillings and two pence. You could save your day
> off and have an annual holiday of twelve days a year. You had
> Sunday morning off from ten o'clock until one; or in the afternoon
> from two onwards. The idea was you went to church, which was in
> the hall, in the theatre. The children went to morning service,
> according to the prayer book, and an evening service in the afternoons.
> So we went twice. You took everybody, they had all paid for a seat
> in church. The Vicar from the local church, St Mark's, would come
> across and take the service. There was a balcony as well in the hall.
> That was the life then, it was a good life, I would say that still.*

This was, of course, in the days before any mechanical adaptations
were installed to assist the staff with the care of the patients – let
alone risk assessments for the nurses:

> *We didn't have a lift in the private days. I can still remember Richard
> in my arms, someone on my back and helping another one up the
> stairs. "Come on you the mother of many, and the wife of none!"
> So you not only carried the physically disabled up the stairs, you
> also took up the wheelchairs, and the spinal carriages. Twice a day!*

Christmas was always celebrated with great vigour and enthusiasm at Normansfield. Even during the war, when lunch had to be taken in the basement, the festivities didn't suffer. One of the staff acted as a lookout on the roof and if there was a warning of enemy planes, he or she would blow a tin whistle. At the beginning of December, *The Evening News* placed an appeal for every child in the hospital to receive a present. The staff used to collect the presents from a warehouse in London. One Christmas, the staff made a sleigh from an old pram and all the presents were placed inside. One of the cooks donned a Father Christmas costume and was given a bell to ring as he approached the house. Nurse Prentice describes the scene:

> *The grounds were beautiful with trees and bushes. We said to the children, "Listen for the bell, Father Christmas is coming!" There was much excitement on hearing the bell and then seeing this red figure come through the trees. Oh, it was the most wonderful thing we ever did.*

The morale of all concerned during these difficult years has been described in several accounts as 'outstanding' and nurse Prentice was particularly impressed by the role of Stella, Lady Brain. Reginald Langdon Down's daughter had married a neurologist, Dr Russell Brain (later Lord Brain) and she and her family moved back to Normansfield to help her father and Percival's wife, Mouche, during the war:

> *Great praise must be given to Dr Langdon Down's daughter - Lady Brain. She fought like a tiger with various local authorities to ensure that, in spite of shortages, we at least got our full share of extras. The Langdon Downs did all they could to ease our lot. Hours of duty were shortened. We also received small wage rises each year and by 1945 we had reached the dizzy heights of £9.10 shillings a month!*

In 1945 there were 160 patients in the main building at Normansfield with an additional 21 women who had been transferred from Conifers. One of these was Margaret (Margot) Rutherford, an extraordinary woman who I visited when I started writing this book. Then aged 104, Margot was a resident of Kingston Road Old People's Home, in the grounds of Normansfield, where she had been admitted when the hospital closed.

Margot was born in Jesmond, Newcastle upon Tyne, in 1899 to Evelyn Alice Rutherford, who also had two other daughters. Her father, Dr Vickerman Henzell Rutherford, was born in 1861 and studied medicine in Edinburgh and Glasgow. On qualifying as a doctor, he joined his father and elder brother in general practice in Newcastle.

In 1903, Dr Rutherford moved to London to take up a political career, pledged to fight for more equitable conditions of life for working people in the great industrial centres. He was elected an MP in 1906, sitting as a Liberal/Labour member for Brentford until 1910. Dr Rutherford's views were very much ahead of his time – particularly in his support for the League of Nations and being in favour of self-government for India.

Margot came down with her parents to London from the northeast and remained in her new home in Regents Park until the age of fifteen when she was admitted to Normansfield. On the date of admission, 22nd December 1914, the following facts were observed by a Dr Bruce Ferguson:

> *She does not know her age states she is only 10 is very confused . . . does not know where she lives and is unable to answer intelligently my questions.*

A Dr Corner added:

> *She is impulsive and spiteful to other children, cannot understand anything she is told. She says she is three days old. She does not know how long she has been here, although she has only been here a few days. She does not know where she comes from and where her home is.*

No doubt because of their Hippocratic connection, (not to mention the customary request for payment) the day after her admission, Reginald Langdon Down wrote to Margot's father:

Margot Rutherford aged 104.

23rd Dec 1914

Dear Dr Rutherford,

I am glad to say that Margaret had a good night and seems to have settled happily. I am sending you the statement of particulars in order that you may add the date of birth. Will you kindly return it to me? I also enclose the memorandum of the a/c for the current quarter. I may mention that our inmates should be provided with 2 pairs of sheets – 4 hand towels – 4 table napkins and 2 bath towels. Will you kindly address any letters or parcels for your little girl 'south wing' Normansfield as the postman delivers there direct.

I am
Yours sincerely

Unfortunately Margot's initial 'happy settling' proved somewhat optimistic as this letter from Reginald Langdon Down reveals:

29th Dec 1914

Dear Dr R

Thank you for your letter enclosing the certificate and your cheque for which I send you a form of acknowledgement. I note what you say as to Mrs Rutherford's wishes with regard to the clothing. We will get the necessary sheets, towels etc. In other respects I am told she is very well provided with the exception of boots which she has only 1 pair and I think I ought to get another pair for her. Since I wrote to you we have had a certain amount of trouble with her at night. She gave way to temper and screamed, pulled her hair and threw things about. On the first occasion we had her removed to the observation room for the night. On the following night she again gave trouble and cried to be removed to the other room, but this we would not give way to and she ultimately settled down for the night. Last night she slept quietly.

By June of the following year, however, Margot had calmed down, was in better health and, no doubt, on best behaviour when her parents visited and took her out for a ride in their motor car. She also went on holiday that July to Bognor and was described as 'behaving better'.

There is also correspondence between Mrs Rutherford and Reginald Langdon Down which she explains that she hasn't been able to reply to him earlier, but this was due to the fact that Dr Rutherford was aboard the *Sussex* which had been attacked by German U-boats in 1916 .

Reginald replied with typical British understatement:

Dear Mrs R

I think you have had a form of receipt for the cheque which you recently sent me, for which I thank you. I quite understand that the matter of my letter must remain over until Dr R has returned home. I am so glad to hear that he escaped safely from the Sussex it must have been a great anxiety to you when you heard it had been torpedoed.

(The torpedoing without warning of the cross-Channel steamer, *Sussex* actually was quite a significant event in the First World War as a number of Americans were killed and injured. President Woodrow Wilson sent a stern communication to the German Government, threatening to break off diplomatic ties. This was a very serious threat and resulted in the Germans stopping the U-boats campaign in British waters.)

On Dr Rutherford's return from France, Margot was misbehaving and Reginald requested that the Rutherfords fund a private room and a nurse to herself so that she might be given individual attention. Dr Rutherford responded by stating that with a reduction in his income and an increase in taxation:

We shall be pleased if you can manage without putting Margot into a separate bedroom. I hope you have better news to give us.

We shall never know quite who was victorious in this financial battle of wills but, in any case, Reginald wrote in July 1916 to report that:

Margot is, I am glad to say, keeping very well indeed. She seems to have thoroughly enjoyed her time at the seaside and is looking brown. Her behaviour just recently shows improvement.

Margot was placed under the Jurisdiction of the Court of Protection in 1920. A report from seven years later states that she is:

> *Quite well behaved during needlework in school . . . behaved very well in Worthing for six weeks.*

In 1934, Dr Rutherford passed away at the age of 73 and his wife nearly 30 later at the age of 97. One of Margot's nephews, Brian Ware, became her official receiver in 1983 and for many years, with the help of his elderly sisters, planned a regular programme of visits at Christmas and birthday celebrations.

Margot was duly transferred from the hospital to the residential home, but remained in the grounds of the hospital in which she had resided since the age of ten. She was clearly frustrated by her learning disability throughout her life and raged against the institutions that housed her. She spoke very little if at all, but the one telling phrase that she repeated constantly to staff and on my visit was:

> *Margot knows . . .*

She died in April 2006, aged 105. She had spent over 90 of these in institutional care.

CHAPTER TWELVE

FRIENDS IN NEED

All are lunatics, but he who can analyse
his delusions is called a philosopher.

Ambrose Bierce, author (1842-1914)

In many ways, post-war Britain provided a new moral direction for disabled people. Eugenics and social Darwinism were finally discredited by their association with the Nazi extermination camps and in the absence of a defined framework, the area of mental handicap now became a health issue. The 1946 National Health Service Act, which came into operation two years later, defined a hospital as an institution for 'the reception and treatment of persons suffering from illness or mental defectiveness' and transferred local authority hospitals to the Ministry of Health.

The National Health Service took over the major responsibility for mental health from county councils and boroughs, the main inheritance being a system of over 100 asylums, or 'mental hospitals', with an average population of over 1,000 patients in each. The Act also ended the distinction between paying and non-paying patients.

In 1951, the Langdon Down family decided that it just wasn't practicable to continue to run Normansfield as private institution. The hospital was suffering very badly from wear and tear and the large sums required for refurbishing and rebuilding were simply not available. Their decision may also have been influenced by the receipt of a letter from the Regional Health Board explaining, 'there may be provision for private patients, but the majority will be health service patients'.

The Langdon Down family were very keen that the residents should not be dispersed or the land disposed of in parts, and it was thus agreed that the hospital should be put on the market. On 22nd June 1951 Normansfield was duly sold to the North West Metropolitan Regional Hospital Board. In fact, some of the 'higher grade' patients were actually moved to other institutions. Conifers and Trematon ceased to be approved homes and some staff retired, but the Langdon Down family involvement with Normansfield continued with the appointment as Medical Superintendent of yet another Langdon Down, Percival's son, Norman, who had been deputy medical Superintendent since 1946.

The Staines Group Hospital Management Committee became the responsible Health Authority and the family connection was further strengthened by the appointment to the management committee of Lady Stella Brain (John Langdon Down's grand-daughter) in 1952.

Norman Langdon Down's wife, Patricia, was interviewed in 2002 and recalls their early days at the hospital,

> *Norman went back to Normansfield shortly after the war on very little money, and we were very poor. He had been a deputy medical superintendent at another large place near here, Brookwood, but came back to Normansfield because he wanted to work there. They were still very kindly, still a lot of nurses. John (her grandfather) had decided that there should be three children to one nurse, like a mother to them. It was still like that a little bit and Norman was full of it. He thought John was wonderful of course. John died when Norman was fifteen.*

Norman Langdon Down was very stoical about the sale. He had realised for a while that it was inevitable and naturally hoped that it was in the patients' best interests. The sale did cause some familial bitterness, however, although it was conducted by an eminent solicitor who also happened to be Norman's brother-in-law. The 40 acres of land that surrounded the buildings were sold and, according to Patricia, the family lost out financially. When the house was sold she tried to persuade Norman to take all the things from his office as she was concerned that they were going to be sold too:

*We even had to go to the sale and buy quite a lot of John Langdon
Down's furniture, as they sold everything, the hospital, land and house!*

After Normansfield moved out of private hands, Norman Langdon
Down continued in his job as Medical Superintendent, running
the whole hospital, but was only paid at the level of senior house
officer. There was also a little friction with Stella Brain, by all
accounts an extremely strong and single minded woman, and
Reginald Langdon Down, who died in 1955. Norman was
exceptionally dedicated to his work. For some years he worked
seven days a week, and Christmas was no exception. He took on
the role of Father Christmas and dispensed presents to the patients.

Norman and Patricia attended winter dances and she would be
greeted by the patients as 'Mrs Norman' – her husband was known
as Dr Norman. Apparently, a visitor once asked to see Dr Langdon
Down, and the attending nurse replied, 'Sorry, we haven't got a
Dr Langdon Down.' She was also under the impression that
Norman was his surname.

Staff at that time were delighted at the way in which the
Langdon Down family negotiated the sale of the hospital. Every
staff member who had completed ten years service were granted
full pension rights, which was of great financial help to the long
term employees who previously had only received a small service
bonus, donated privately by Dr Langdon Down.

At this time, the formidable Miss Cleke retired and a new matron
and nursing sister were employed. The working hours of the nurses
were shortened and their wages increased. Accommodation in the
form of a nurses home was set aside and uniforms were provided.
Inevitably, the old 'family system' came to an end and the staff no
longer slept-in with the patients. The children were looked after by
whichever group of nurses were on duty, rather than receiving the
very personalised care to which they had become accustomed.

In her interview, Nurse Hall described the transition as traumatic
and painful for patients and staff alike:

> *I must be honest and admit that the new benefits we received
> were welcome in many ways but the "red tape" spread its tentacles
> everywhere and nearly strangled us. I remained at Normansfield
> for many more years but always regretted the passing of the old days.*

As I have already stated, we worked long and demanding hours for low
wages but, surprising as it may seem, we were content we were one big
family. If I had my time over again, I would do exactly the same.
The love that was returned to us by these children is beyond compare.

An extremely active and lucrative League of Friends of
Normansfield was formed in 1957 by Lady Brain, who became
President. A friend of hers, Colonel Symons, was elected
Chairman. Over £100,000 was raised in the next few years to
provide amongst other things, a school, a shop and club room for
the patients, a hydrotherapy pool, and a holiday home, Bill House,
at Selsey, Sussex.

The following is taken from *The League of Friends Of Normansfield*
Booklet (1964) and provides engaging if somewhat quaint 'pen
pictures' of the erstwhile committee:

LADY BRAIN

In the same year that Normansfield became state controlled, Lady
Brain became a member of the Staines Group management
Committee and a year later in 1952, she was elected to the South
West Metropolitan Regional Hospital Board.

COLONEL P A SYMONS MC JP

Has been a resident of Teddington for 57 years. A military man
with a fine record in both world wars with Colonel Symons in the
chair, the agenda is pleasantly and resolutely tackled. When the
discussion wanders off course it is brought back to target area with
the deft touch of experience. Under the camouflage of a keen wit he
will bend the rules to find a short cut objective.

DOCTOR N LANGDON DOWN

Called affectionately Dr Norman.

MRS I M SHERREN

Our honorary Secretary – you cannot dim this lady's spirits no
matter how many times she is on the wrong end of "over to you".
She now realises the thankless and responsible job she's landed.

R W E GILBERT

Honorary Treasurer and before retirement Manager of Westminster Bank, Kingston on Thames. We are indeed fortunate that the administration of our resources rests in such capable hands. Not withstanding his capabilities, he is often unable to meet the demands made upon him for funds. He would need to be capable of mystifying the magic Circle to meet those demands, but the influence this jolly gentleman does wield over our matters of monies make him indispensable.

B RIX

A strikingly successful man in all he undertakes. He is more widely known as "That extremely active West End actor-manager at the Whitehall Theatre", but not a little of his time and energy is spent raising funds for handicapped children. To be in committee with Brian Rix is to be in orbit from where everything is possible and within reach.

MRS B RIX

Elspet Gray to those whose pleasure it is to watch her from an auditorium, But Mrs Rix to those whose added pleasure it is to know her. She and her husband are a team within a team, sometimes disagreeing with each other but always reaching complete understanding with a firm resolve.

E H C HENSHALL

Who admits to these writings and takes this opportunity to express his pleasure at being in such good company for such a worthwhile cause.

The League of Friends was a very effective and energetic body within the institution and was understandably not exactly modest in pointing out its achievements:

In six and a half years since its inception the record of accomplishment is impressive. Collections have provided funds for chairs for the concert hall, television sets, coach trips to the seaside. Other items

157

include a tennis court, a paved playground, and a mini bus. The
League, each year, invites the staff to a show and supper, an event
which gives pleasure to hosts and guests alike.

In 1958, when the league had been formed a little more than a year, the Committee decided that it was ready to tackle its first big project, the building of a school within the hospital grounds. In 1961 the Stella Brain School was opened and handed over to the hospital.

There is a fascinating description of the school in the 1964 booklet, very much of its time:

During the summer a lot of activity is out of doors. A great favourite
is the pony and the riding lessons. Rumours will have it that the
pony is going to have a foal next year. What fun that will be!

There is definite shape to the life of the 60 or so patients who go
to school. There is the boy who was so difficult that nothing could
be done for him. Now his ability has been discovered; he just loves
to paste paper bags and so sits patiently and nothing will deter him
from his duties. There is the elderly patient who had lost all purpose
in life and even forgot how to walk. Now she makes baskets and
walks on her own again. There is the star pupil of them all: he made
such progress that he is now taken daily by bus to a special school.

Although in operation for a few months only, the school has
proved to be of immense help as nurses can give remaining patients
more attention when 60 of them are taken off their hands each day.

The Stella Brain school.

Matron, Norman Langdon Down and Lady Brain.

'Gordon', a former pupil, remarked that when he was naughty in the school, the punishment would be to sit in the corner with his hands on his head. He also enjoyed the annual sports day when the residents would compete in running races and a tug-of-war competition. The League next directed its thoughts to include those ineducable patients who were unable to benefit from the school and decided on its second major scheme – the establishment of a holiday home by the sea. A most suitable house was quickly found in Sussex on the tip of Selsey Bill:

> *Bill House was contracted to the League of Friends and before the end of 1963 three quarters of the patients at Normansfield had spent two weeks holiday on the Sussex coast. The house, which stood in two acres of lawns and flower beds, was entirely secluded and accessible only from a private lane or the beach. The owner of the property, the delightfully named Mr England Liddiard, cut the market price by half for the hospital, allowed three years for payment and donated furnishings and gardening equipment worth over fifteen hundred pounds.*

It is hard to disagree with the comment, however self-praising, from the League of Friends that:

> Reports indicate that the Bill House and the Stella Brain school have brought happiness, health and new interests to the patients of Normansfield.

The League of Friends was fortunate to have the theatrical Rix's on board. With their boundless energy, a steadfast commitment to the cause and a contact list of show business celebrities that was the envy of Val Parnell, the couple proved indispensable. The staff also benefited, with free tickets to the Whitehall Theatre and Bertram Mills Circus amongst other entertainments.

Brian and Elspet Rix were first introduced to the world of disability in 1951 when their daughter, Shelley, was born with Down's syndrome. Brian Rix openly recalls in his first auto-biography, *My Farce From My Elbow*:

> Shelley went to a private home where she remained for the first five years of her life. That was the norm in those days. If you had the resources, the advice you received was to thank your lucky stars, put your mentally handicapped son or daughter in private care and get on with raising the normal members of your family.

At the age of five, Shelley was admitted to Normansfield for which the couple were extremely grateful.

> Even after the NHS had taken over, the clientele were generally selected from the same-upper crust background so, as actors, I suppose we were lucky to have been considered. Even so Shelley had to be certified – for she was entering a state hospital – and the memory of that dreadful process, conducted by two London County Council doctors, will remain with us always.

Brian and Elspet were incensed by the insensitivity of the procedure, particularly at the treatment Shelley received from one of the doctors, who barked orders at her, thrust aptitude tests at her, and at the same time showing complete disapproval. They felt humiliated at the way they had to drag her through the bureaucratic processes demanded by the archaic 1913 mental deficiency legislation:

> *She had to prove she was mentally handicapped even though at that time she could neither walk nor talk.*

Brian Rix was even asked if he had venereal disease or was drunk at the time of conception.

Following Shelley's admission, Mr and Mrs Rix threw themselves into various fundraising events. The Annual Ball was a real money-spinner, held initially at the Hyde Park Hotel and then moved to the Dorchester for reasons of space. Brian Rix writes:

> *The Normansfield Ball was initially an experimental event as far I was concerned. We charged two guineas and made six hundred . . . we were always fundraising. It's no wonder we had difficulty in keeping our friends. We were always selling them tickets!'*

The cabaret line up over the years included such stars as Harry Secombe, Tommy Cooper, Vera Lynn, Dudley Moore, Rolf Harris Frankie Howerd, Cleo Laine, Danny La Rue, Alfred Marks, Alma Cogan, Dickie Henderson, Peter Cook and Dudley More.

Meanwhile, the hospital itself needed modernisation, and money for repairing and upgrading the buildings was made available. This included the building of new day rooms in 1960, the installation of a new central heating system, rewiring, the conversion of an old farm building into an industrial unit, and the construction of two new yards and a block of staff flats. This further increased the number of patients to 238.

In 1971, responsibility for the education of children resident in the hospital was divested to the London Borough of Richmond-upon-Thames. A few children attended local special schools, while the Normansfield Education Unit now run by the local education authority transferred to Trematon in 1974.

There were also two important changes to the terminology relating to patients at Normansfield and beyond: The 1959 Mental Health Act used the terms 'subnormal' and 'severely subnormal' for the first time (not exactly a breakthrough in sensitivity, but a step towards 'mental handicap' and the now acceptable 'people with learning difficulties'); Two years later, there was a move to banish the concept of 'racial degeneracy', which had shaped policy for 'mental defectives'.

In 1961, Norman Langdon Down and eighteen international experts in the disability field wrote to the medical journal, *The Lancet* suggesting that the name 'Mongolian Idiot' should be changed to 'Down's syndrome'. It took four years for this petition to have any impact, but in 1965, at the request of the People's Republic of Mongolia, the World Health Organisation agreed to this suggestion and Down's syndrome then became a globally accepted term.

Other aspects of care for the disabled still needed updating. For years physical restraint was seen as fair treatment for patients who proved difficult to control. To be fair to the staff at Normansfield it was quite rare for residents to suffer this fate. Nevertheless, the hospital produced a booklet entitled, *A Register of Mechanical Restraints and Seclusion, 1946-1960*. The publication, fortunately a slim volume, describes a few problems such as 'restlessness, destructive tendencies, tearing clothes and attempts to escape'. Time spent in seclusion was between one and twelve hours in total

DANGEROUS LIAISONS?

Over the years, an institution the size of Normansfield must have, witnessed a huge number of romances. Most, of course, we shall never know about, but a couple of the relationships have since become Hampton Wick folklore: Phoebe Burgess was a widow, who worked as a clerk to Matrons Bunsten and Bourne for a year and a half in the mid-1960's. She met her second husband, Don, at a dance at Normansfield, which was held in the theatre. They had apparently been eyeing each other up for a large part of the evening but only summoned up the courage to dance the last waltz together. They started going out soon very soon after and now Don gets a kick out of telling people that they met in an asylum.

A far less tender story is that of the amorous staff gardener who was regularly allowed to have his wicked way with one of the less alluring patients in return for a packet of cigarettes. This dangerous liaison continued for some months until he reneged on the deal and withheld the required cigarettes. The disgruntled resident immediately reported him and the man of the soil was summarily dismissed.

Who said there was no smoke without fire?

but used frequently for the same few individuals. The only restraints recorded were either to the arms or legs and used to prevent scratching for people with eczema.

The question of personal freedom in relation to institutional care and communal living was highlighted by two tragic deaths, both reported in *The Times*, while Norman Langdon Down was Medical Superintendent.

Christopher William Tomlins was admitted to Normansfield in February 1953 at the age of nine when in the care of his father. Christopher was first described as 'backward' at the age of five and his admission notes describe:

> . . . *an imbecile, can't recognise letters, count or tell the time, no recognition of money, can't dress himself, noisy and disruptive, undresses himself, can't play with toys.*

Christopher settled in well initially, but was described as noisy, spiteful and rough with fellow patients. 'He is frequently faulty in his habits.'

Sadly, Christopher's stay at Normansfield and, indeed his life, was all too short:

INQUEST ON BOY MENTAL PATIENT

A verdict of accidental death was recorded at an inquest at Kingston-on-Thames yesterday on Christopher William Tomlins, aged 9, a patient in a mental institution, who was found drowned in the Thames at Teddington on Monday.

Dr Norman Langdon Down, a medical superintendent at Normansfield, Kingston Road, Teddington, said that it was easy for a patient to get out of the home. There was no sort of roll call.

Recording the verdict, Dr C F J Baron, the coroner, said, "It is apparently the policy of this institution and, I believe, of most other similar institutions, that there shall be no locked doors and that, virtually, patients shall be free to move as they wish. I express no sort of opinion as to whether that policy is a good one or not, but it seems clear that following that policy, this boy did get out and was drowned".

The Times, 31 December 1953

Fifteen years later, in *The Times* edition of 5th September 1968, under the headline, *"MISCHIEF" DEATH IN WARD*, another terrible event was reported:

> *A verdict of Death by Misadventure was recorded yesterday at an inquest on a mental patient, whose death was said to have been caused by a 'mischievous' boy patient.*
>
> *'Mr Peter Oakley, a severe spastic, aged 24, died of a fractured skull when the boy tipped him out of his chair at Normansfield Hospital, Teddington, Middlesex.*
>
> *The inquest, at Kingston upon Thames, Surrey, was told that the boy aged 15, was subnormal, but active and generally destructive, causing trouble with other patients. He was not responsible for his actions.*
>
> *Dr Norman Langdon-Down, medical superintendent at the hospital, was asked what could be done to prevent the boy from damaging other patients. He replied: "We have to keep a sharp eye on him."*
>
> *Asked what staff were in the ward of 70 patients, some of them active, Dr Langdon-Down said it varied. Usually there were three or four nurses.*
>
> *The coroner, Mr John Burton asked: "Is that all?" Later, he commented that there seemed to be no way of preventing such incidents of death, except by moving active members of mental hospitals to another form of custody.*
>
> *Dr Langdon-Down, asked if anyone had considered a transfer for the boy, replied: "No." He added: "it would be extremely difficult to find anywhere to send him." The doctor said one idea would be to have a special ward for such patients as the boy. The hospital did not have one, although he believed that some larger places had.*
>
> *Another way of dealing with the problem, Dr Langdon-Down said, would be to have more staff. But it would be difficult to get them and it was already difficult to keep up the establishment.*
>
> *Mr William Nordberg, a charge nurse, told the inquest that the boy was 'mischievous all the time.'*
>
> *Acting Detective-Inspector John Cresswell said no criminal proceedings were being taken.*

An unusual legal case also concerning a Normansfield patient was heard at the Court of Appeal in April 1957 before Lord Justices Denning, Parker and Sellers. Ralph Edward Gosselin Richardson had been detained in various institutions for over 30 years, but had originally been detained at Normansfield on the 12th February 1925 on order of Thomas Coote JP on petition of Ralph's mother, Aileen Richardson. The statutory declarator stated, 'He is neglected as it is impossible for his parents who reside in India to provide care and control.' Mr Richardson had been a resident at Brook House, Southgate, between 1923 and 1925, where he was described as:

> . . . *lazy, doing little work and generally neglectful of himself and his appearance, He is unable to concentrate, given to masturbation, always trying to find fault with others. Not epileptic or suicidal or dangerous to others.*

The young man was seen by a Harley Street doctor at the end of 1924 and was then described as having 'no continuity of thought and possessing grandiose ideas'. Mr Richardson had been educated at public schools but at the age of eighteen had suffered a breakdown.

> *Having recently failed employment on a poultry farm (nothing more than a slacker) he thinks he could succeed on railway service or medicine. He has little idea of the value of money. Says he pawned his bicycle for 10 shillings and when in London obtains two shillings from his mother for the pictures and spent half a crown on going home with a prostitute.*

On his admission to Normansfield at the beginning of the following year, Richardson fell ill with influenza and was confined to bed. Following his recovery, he was put under direction of the head gardener Mr Dymoth to work on the farm. Mr Dymoth stated that Ralph lacked common sense even with simple jobs.

On 3rd March 1925, house worker Mrs Russell bid, 'Good morning Mr Richardson, how are you this morning?' He replied, "I am better thank you but they call me 'Ralph'." Next morning she called him 'Ralph' and he replied, "My name is Richardson." Two weeks later he was put to work with the cook, who was equally unimpressed, commenting that he would rather have an imbecile to work with him!

On 14th October 1925 Ralph was transferred to Rampton Hospital in Nottinghamshire, a high-secure institution for people of dangerous, violent or criminal propensities. But he was advised:

> *This is to inform you that the visitors have not ordered your discharge and if you wish you may appeal to this board about this decision within fourteen days from now. Should you decide to make an appeal I will forward it.*

Right up to discharge there were still complaints from staff about his language and his obsession with sex, constantly asking about the price of a prostitute and 'threatening to bring one in from Kingston'.

Somewhat belatedly, in fact over 30 years later, Ralph Gosselin Richardson did challenge the Board of Control's decision on the grounds of alleged breach of statutory duty and negligence. He was initially turned down and so approached the Court of Appeal.

In this hearing, Lord Justice Denning recounted that Richardson had been found to be beyond the care of his parents who were prepared to certify him as 'a mental defective'. Middlesex Council had taken him to a place of safety under section fifteen of the Mental Deficiency Act of 1913 as a person 'found neglected'. A specially appointed magistrate had decreed that Mr Richardson was 'a feeble minded person, a defective within the meaning of the Act. He was neglected and not under care and control'. Under the Act Ralph Richardson had been detained at Normansfield.

Soon after, his father had died and his mother could no longer pay for his keep at Normansfield. He had to be transferred somewhere and as Middlesex County Council could pay for him, he was moved to Rampton in October 1925. The Board of Control had made an order that he was 'of dangerous propensities'. After three decades of incarceration, Mr Richardson now sought to bring an action complaining that, from the beginning, his detention had been unlawful.

Richardson's legal advisors claimed that the appeal was based on the fact that written consent should have been obtained from Richardson's father, instead of solely his mother. However, as Mr Richardson Sr had been in India at the time of the order, Lord

Denning doubted whether, in law, the consent of the father was necessary at the time . He could not see any substantial grounds for the contention against the Board on this point.

It is the summing up by Lord Denning, a renowned reformer, that is somewhat chilling:

> *It was an unfortunate feature of mental illness that those affected by it sometimes did not realise the need for being under care and control. They resented it, much as a small child or a dumb animal resented being given medicine for their own good, and they were apt to turn round and bite and scratch and claw those giving it. So here Mr Richardson had turned round on his own mother. Yet if any impartial person looked at the facts they would have seen that this poor woman was at her wits end to know what to do with the boy. She was now aged 81 and one good thing was that her son had not sought fit to inflict on her an action for damages, though if his case was true she was the cause and origin of all his troubles. If he were a man of sound mind, he would be worthy of condemnation, but as he was a sick creature, feeble minded and incapable of telling right from wrong, the court could forgive him. It seemed to his Lordship that no substantial ground was shown here and the appeal of the proposed plaintiff should be dismissed.*

So Ralph Edward Gosselin Richardson remained institutionalised until his death.

In 1970, the much respected Norman Langdon Down stepped down as Medical Superintendent. His retirement party was reported in *The Twickenham Times* on 19 June 1970:

NORMANSFIELD SUPERVISOR SAYS GOODBYE

Comedy actor Brian Rix, and his wife Elspet Gray, were guests at a Sherry party at Normansfield hospital, Teddington, on Wednesday night, to mark the retirement of the hospital supervisor. Dr. Norman Langdon-Down. The party was given by the Staines hospital management committee, and the hospital staff are giving the doctor a party on Saturday June 27th. Mr Rix, whose 18-years-old

*daughter, Shelley, is a patient at the hospital said: "I have known
Dr. Langdon-Down for the best part of 16 years and I have always
found him an enormously helpful man and kind. It is sad in a
service which has great difficulty in recruiting that there is an
arbitrary age limit when a man has to retire. I am sure Dr.
Langdon-Down has many years' service left to give." After his
medical training, Dr Langdon-Down joined the navy in 1943,
and after the war he came to Normansfield as deputy medical
supervisor to his father.*

Elspet Rix described Norman Langdon Down as:

> *. . . a lovely man, who was part of, and therefore understood the
> family traditions of the institution and thus the way it should work.*

It is clear that Norman Langdon Down held true affection for the
institution and there is no doubt that he was truly shocked and
saddened by events after his departure. For within a few years of his
retirement, the state of affairs at Normansfield had seriously
deteriorated.

The Friends of Normansfield had realised that something was
wrong since 1974, but every time they attempted to advise the Area
Health Authority of the problem they were told that it was really
none of the business of the League of Friends.

At the AGM in November 1974, vice-chairman Eric Henshall
reported:

> *A system of administration now exists which seems to have
> gradually taken away the warmth and understanding which
> hitherto existed between parents and hospital staff. Our real
> concern is the widening distance and changing wavelength in
> communications between ourselves and the hospital. The basic
> blame for this situation, we are sure, has to be levelled against the
> administration.*

This was just the beginning of a traumatic period in the history of
Normansfield and, indeed, there would be much blame to be
levelled in the coming years.

CHAPTER THIRTEEN

A DISTILLERY, SEVERAL BALLOONISTS AND A REDHEAD

4th Oct 1907

Dear sir

I am anxious to place my little girl aged four years in some establishment where she could be taken care of and Dr Savage has mentioned your name to me saying that you undertake the charge of children whose brain has not developed. I shall be glad to know whether you could consider a proposal to take charge of my little child and if so perhaps you could give me some idea of your charges and also tell me at what hour you could see me any day soon.

On hearing from you I would arrange to call upon you at N.

John Dunville

This rather simple letter sealed the fate of a young girl, who, in other circumstances, would have experienced an extraordinarily privileged life. Una Dunville was born on 22nd February 1903. She had Down's syndrome and lived with her parents at 46 Portland Place, London.

It appears that once 'JD' (Una's father, John Dunville)

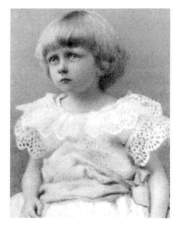

received a positive response form Normansfield, he acted promptly:

> *15th Oct 1907*
>
> *My wife and I have decided to ask you to take charge of our little girl and if you can arrange to take her on Nov 2nd we would bring her to you. I will send you the papers which you gave me for signature when I hear from you. Your terms would I understand be 250 Guineas per annum.*
>
> *John Dunville*

However, the decision to institutionalise Una having cared for their daughter for over four years of her life was obviously heart-rending and needed arranging speedily:

> *16th Oct 1907*
>
> *Since writing to you proposing that you should take charge of our little girl on 2nd Nov, my wife has expressed her desire that the matter should be settled at the earliest date and I therefore write to ask you to let me know the earliest date on which you could arrange to view the child. I think that my wife, having at last reluctantly made up her mind that she must be parted from the child, is anxious that it should not be delayed.*
>
> *John Dunville*

Before the end of the month, Una was duly taken to Normansfield and took up residency in the girls' south wing. The following was written on admission:

> *Sent by Dr Savage at 4 yrs. Is like a child of two, walks does not speak, can indicate wants, incontinent, difficulty in swallowing, stuffy in nose and throat, rather spiteful, has three brothers, not fond of music, recognises rhythm, used to hang her tongue out and still occasionally, short neck, hair down her back . . . does not play well with toys throws them, does tear clothes, very determined, good natured, never been ill, won't take medicine, frightened of having her hair cut, when she screams she is sick, never could be left alone.*

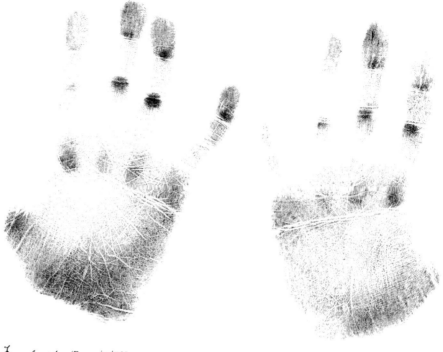

Female of 17   6-'03
medium grade mental defective
mongol type - red hair.

Una had her handprint made and a picture was taken in 1920. Next to the handprint it also says 'red hair'. A further entry made on 7th November 1931, which states that she was discharged and re-admitted on the same day remarks that she is 'a mongol type'.

Within several months of admission, Una's mother, Violet Dunville, now felt able to correspond with Percival Langdon Down:

> *Hotel Stern*
>
> *Dear Dr Down,*
>
> *It's time for me to write and thank you for all your letters about baby. You are always so good in letting me know and I never will write to bother you. I am so happy that she is so well now and I do hope when I get back from here in a fortnight you will allow me to*

go down to see her. I always am wondering if she knows any more things than she did. I expect after such a long time I shall see a change in her – I am here bathing and drinking.

Dunville is in London and busy with his balloon . . .

With Kind regards to you both

Yours sincerely

Violet Dunville

Despite her busy pursuit of field sports, Mrs Dunville was true to her word and visited Una at Normansfield:

Arisaig House
Arisaig RSO
Invernesshire

I never like bothering you with letters as I know you are so good about writing to me and no news is good news. I feel still as I am here I should like to know a little about poor Una and how she is since I saw her. We were so sorry we did not see you. But very happy to see her so well and happy in herself.

I have been fishing, hunting and stalking, shot two stags myself.

Violet Dunville

These letters provide some clues to Una's fascinating family background. She was the fourth child of Lieutenant Colonel and Wing Commander John Dunville CBE, MA (Cantab), DL, RAF, and Violet Anne Blanche Dunville, née Lambart of 46 Portland Place, London and Redburn House, Holywood, County Down. The couple married in 1892 and had three other children: Robert (Bobby), John and William Gustavus. The family household in London consisted of twelve servants, a butler, two footmen, a lady's maid, a cook, two nurses, two housemaids, two kitchen maids and a hall boy.

The summer months and Christmas were spent at Redburn House in County Down, Ireland (Northern Ireland after 1921), which was looked after by sixteen house staff and ten ground staff. The stables housed 60 horses for hunting and four horses for drawing carriages all tended by sixteen grooms.

Una Dunville with her mother, Violet, and brother, Robert (Bobby).

In addition to the house at Redburn, Holywood, the couple also had a residence, Sion House, near Navan, County Meath. Although Violet Dunville was more than comfortably off in her own right, the family fortune was mainly due to the wealth of John's father, Robert Grimshaw Dunville, who was chairman of Dunville and Co., Ltd., an old established Belfast firm of distillers. Employees of Dunville's formed a cricket club in 1879 and in the following year the famous Distillery Football Club.

Colonel and Mrs John Dunville and unknown passenger in 'Banshee III' at Solbosch, Brussels, 15th July 1924.

John Dunville was actually a renowned Edwardian aeronaut. In his balloon *La Mascotte* he was a leading contestant in the United Kingdom Point-To-Point race of 1908, setting off from the Hurlingham Club, Chelsea. He was reported as flying so low that he was able to ask directions of motorists and pedestrians! He subsequently devoted much of his attention to the pursuit of the cirrus and cumulus, and became a prominent and daring balloonist, competing in a number of international events. In November 1908, Dunville also piloted the first balloon to cross the English Channel with four passengers. One of his passengers was his wife, Violet. Some years previously, in 1890, the Cambridge educated Dunville was appointed Political Private Secretary to the Duke of Devonshire, whose title in Ulster was the Marquis of Hartington, founder of the Liberal Unionist party. Mr Dunville continued to fill this office until the late Duke's death in 1908 and was later appointed 'Deputy-lieutenant of the County of Down'.

Rosemary Bradley was Assistant Warden of Redburn Country Park, which is on the land that belonged to the Dunville family. She has written about the Dunville family and reported that:

*Una was always a mystery figure in a very private family. I managed
to interview a gentleman who had grown up on the Redburn estate.
He was the first one to mention to me that Una had Down's
syndrome and talked of her remaining at the estate when the rest
of the family went to the season in London. His mother was the
laundress on the estate and he also mentioned that Una was very
well liked by the staff, who also seemed to hold the whole family in
high regard and he talked of Una walking the grounds with either
her nanny or nurse although her face was covered by a form of veil
attached to her hat. Una did, however, appear to have gone with
the family to the estate in Navan for part of the summer. So she
wasn't totally shunned at a time when society was not as
enlightened towards a condition such as Down's syndrome.*

*It's interesting to note that Una played some active part in the
family at a young age and before her admission to Normansfield.
One hopes the fact that her face covered by a veil was not to hide
her features. Certainly the photograph and painting of Una do not
show any obvious characteristics of Down's syndrome. It is possible
however that outside the family and a few members of the Dunville
staff, Una's diagnosis was kept a secret. An action that is by no
means uncommon throughout the history of disability.*

When Violet Dunville wasn't accompanying her husband in his
plucky ballooning adventures, she continued to communicate with
Normansfield throughout 1908, imploring the staff to choose hats
and bonnets that will suit Una:

*I want her to look as nice as if she was at home. I should like blue
ribbon for her . . . please let her wear the little diamond crescent
brooch which she has and her brothers wore. I thought her so much
improved when I saw her.*

Violet also regularly arranged for toys to be delivered (from
Hamley's, of course) and sent her objects from home, such as an
old chair in which Una used to like to sit. Violet always ends her
letters stating how grateful she is for the care that her daughter is
receiving at Normansfield – 'her surroundings are all so nice I
think' – and as the months pass, she states that she feels 'confident
and happier' about Una being away from home.

In 1911, Violet's eldest son, Robert, was suffering from measles, which prevented her from visiting, but she is grateful for photographs of Una that the Langdons sent her although for some reason she would 'prefer it if they could bring the hair down above the forehead.' She goes on to say:

> *I would have written before but since Saturday have been waiting on the winds. We started across the Channel on Sunday and did 180 miles and got back here at 11 last night. It was lovely, we were right above the clouds when we came to the coast.'*

At the beginning of February in the following year, Violet writes from 46 Portland Place:

> *I am sending a little pram for Una which will you please keep for her birthday on the 22nd of this month. I saw her the other day and I was so pleased with her in every way she looked so nice and beautifully turned out, but I was utterly sorry I could not take her away with me, but I know she is in the best keeping . . . No ballooning . . . and hunting impossible this week. I hope you have been skating!!!*

A series of letters between 1913 and 1916 from Percival Langdon Down to the Dunvilles exhibits the level of care, attention and education that Una received at Normansfield:

> *Dear Mrs Dunville,*
>
> *I enclose the usual monthly account for Una who I am glad to say is keeping very well. She has recently been to have her eyes tested again and has some fresh glasses which I hope will help her. She has gone out to 2 or 3 entertainments. She is beginning to read a few of the shortest words.*

> *Dear Mr Dunville,*
>
> *I enclose the usual memorandum of a/c for Una who I am glad to say is keeping well. She is I think making progress in various ways and has been out to 1 or 2 entertainments lately and is looking forward to going to a concert on Sat next.*

Keeping well. Enjoyed visit to Bognor and various amusements donkey riding, pony rides and going to the pictures. She is still making progress and her intelligence is distinctly greater than it was.

Mr Dunville,

Una very well . . . in order to counteract the tendency to lateral curvature of the spine she is lying down for an hour each day on a back board which keeps her spine straight. She has been to see the skating in the park and the pictures in Kingston. Much looking forward to her birthday. The gigantic cracker that you sent provided much pleasure for her and also many companions.

Care also had to be taken of Una's jewellery, which was catalogued by hospital staff and consisted of the following:

Miss Dunville's Jewels

South Wing
Normansfield Hampton Wick

1 watch, 1 gold chain, 2 gold pendants chains, 1 coral necklace, 1 coral necklet, 1 necklet of stones, and 1 case.

One wonders what the motives of families like the Dunvilles were in placing children like Una in institutional care. She lived in both family homes for over four years and yet with all various staff members such as nurses, nannies and servants etc, it was felt that Una needed to be looked after residentially. Many of the families did this for positive reasons – they genuinely did believe that their loved-one could be better cared for by experts, and certainly in most cases contact was maintained by visits and correspondence. Many of the children returned home for decent periods of time. And yet it is somewhat disconcerting to realise that Una doesn't seem to have been home on any visits during her time at Normansfield, even at Christmas or on her birthday.

One reason for the hospitalisation of their children was to protect them and arrange shelter from the outside world which could be extremely cruel. Some patients were, however, felt to be an embarrassment to their families and needed to be invisible to the outside world.

At this time in particular, Una and many other children did need to be protected from a world that was in turmoil. A letter written by Violet in February 1916 summed up the nation's mood:

> *I am so glad to hear from your last letter that Una is well right now.*
> *If I had been in London, I would have gone to see Una. . . all my*
> *family busy fighting for their country.*
>   *But it's all such heart rending . . . How I long for peace.*
>
> *Hope you are all well.*
>
> *Violet Dunville*

The letter also proved to be sadly prophetic. Within six months, the Dunvilles' middle son, Lieutenant John Spencer Dunville, VC, was killed at the age of 21. The following is reproduced from the Dunville family history website:

> *The late Lieut. John Spencer Dunville of the 1st Royal Dragoons*
> *was one of that distinguished band of young Ulstermen who, by*
> *their marked gallantry, won that supreme tribute to British heroism,*
> *the Victoria Cross, during the Great War. It was awarded, as the*
> *official record states: 'For most conspicuous bravery near Epehy,*
> *France, on 24th and 25th June, 1917. When in charge of a party*
> *consisting of scouts and Royal Engineers engaged in the demolition*
> *of the enemy's wire, this officer displayed great gallantry and*
> *disregard of all personal danger. In order to ensure the absolute*
> *success of the work entrusted to him, Second-Lieut. Dunville placed*
> *himself between an NCO. of the Royal Engineers and the enemy's*
> *fire, and thus protected, this NCO was enabled to complete a work*
> *of great importance. Second-Lieut. Dunville, although severely*
> *wounded, continued to direct his men in the wire cutting and*
> *general operations until the raid was successfully completed, thereby*
> *setting a magnificent example of courage, determination, and*
> *devotion to duty to all ranks under his command. The gallant*
> *officer has since succumbed to his wounds.'*

Una's father, meanwhile, had joined the Royal Naval Air Service as a Flight Lieutenant and was soon promoted to Flight Commander. In June 1917 he commanded Number One Balloon Training Wing, Roehampton, and had 450 officers and 2,000 men under his command for training. Although not a million miles away from Teddington, there is no evidence that Wing Commander Dunville visited his daughter, although he was concerned with her welfare:

11.4.18

Royal Naval Air Station Roehampton

I am very anxious about Una and shall be so much obliged if you will telephone me on Putney 2510 tomorrow morning to say how she is. I am living here so you can always get a message to me.

J D

John Dunville was demobilised in September 1919 and was awarded the CBE for his services during the war. Along with son, Robert, he continued to compete in balloon races, notably for the wonderfully named 'Coupe Aéronautique Gordon Bennett'. A letter from Percival Langdon Down on 24th January 1924, addressed legal requirements under the Mental Deficiency Act of 1913 and suggested John Dunville make a representation to the clerk of 'the visitors', Guildhall, Westminster, that Una be allowed to stay at Normansfield. By now Mr Dunville had taken on the rank of Colonel from his previous army service:

Col Dunville

Una, as you know, comes of age on Feb 22nd and I send you the enclosed letter which I am required to do so as a matter of form. There is no doubt the visitors will consider her a suitable case for continued detention here.

In response, the Colonel wrote:

I have seen your letter and under the circumstances I don't think it will be necessary for me to communicate with the clerk. There can be no question of the desirability of Una remaining under your care. If you think that any further action on my part is necessary will you please send me a time to 46 Portland Place. Mrs Dunville has not been very well and I hope to take her for a voyage to South Africa sailing on Feb 29th.

THE MENTAL DEFICIENCY ACT OF 1913

The 1913 Mental Deficiency Act was intended to provide for the care and protection of the mentally defective and established four classes of mental deficiency:

Idiot: unable to guard themselves against common physical dangers such as fire, water or traffic; probably with an IQ of less than 50.

Imbecile: could guard against physical dangers but were incapable of managing themselves or their affairs; probably with an IQ of between 50 and 70.

Feeble-minded: needed care or control for protection of self or others; probably with an IQ of about 70.

Moral defectives: who had vicious or criminal propensities, including unmarried mothers.

The Act also gave local authorities powers to place people having sex outside of marriage into institutions. Homosexuals and people of transgender were also covered. Following the Act a Board of Control was established to take on the powers and responsibilities of the Lunacy Commissioners.

Una, needless to say, remained at Normansfield and with the business end of her 21st birthday sorted, it was time to celebrate with a coming of age dance in her honour. Violet was very grateful:

> *April 1924*
>
> *I feel I must write and thank you and Mrs Down for all your kindness to Una on her birthday – I went down there today to see her having returned from South Africa. I was delighted at the improvement in her every way . . . she dressed up in her birthday clothes and the lovely cap Mrs Down kindly gave her . . . she looked so nice I thought. Miss Cheek (matron) gave me a graphic description of the whole entertainment. I wished I could have seen it. I saw Dr Percival for a few moments.*
>
> *Violet Dunville*

In June 1928, John Dunville died. A letter from Reginald, dated 11th June 1928, offered sincere sympathy and the comforting words, 'fortunately Una will not feel it as much as another would'.

Each Christmas, Violet Dunville sent a number of presents to Una and in addition a large cracker for other residents which always prompted an appreciative letter in return:

21st Jan 1930

Dear Mrs Dunville,

Una is in good health and has very much enjoyed the various Christmas festivities. The large cracker you so kindly sent was a great source of pleasure.

Poor Una had all her teeth removed in the first half of 1930 (at a cost of seventeen guineas) and although she was, according to hospital staff, apparently 'none the worse for it', she was kept in bed. Violet was sympathetic:

I am very sorry to hear about poor little Una whom I have not seen for so long but know she is safe with you. I am staying here with Bobby and also I have moved from my dear old home at '46' to a smaller house not far off at 76 Portland Place and it is all very uphill work.

Every kind wishes

Violet Dunville

The last proposed and recorded visit of Violet Dunville to see Una is on December 9th 1930:

Thanks so much for writing to me about Una and I now know I feel I must go and see her but I really felt from my own feelings . . . I did not care to go. I feel you will understand and I have been a long time in Ireland at both homes. I only came back last Friday with Bobby and his nice wife and they are up to their eyes and preparing for their departure on Friday early for Australia to see Billy . . . if I do not hear to the contrary I will go down Friday afternoon and do hope I shall find Una better.

Hope you and yours are flourishing.

Violet Dunville

Violet was traumatised by another family tragedy when her son, Robert, died in January 1931 and another letter of condolence was penned by Reginald Langdon Down:

> *I was much pained and shocked to hear of the further misfortune that has befallen you in the death of Bobby so unexpectedly. Please accept my most sincere sympathy in which Mrs Percival Langdon Down and my wife join me. Miss Cheek told Una in such simple ways as she can understand what has happened to her.*

Violet was clearly distraught:

> *Redburn*
>
> *19th Feb1931*
>
> *My grateful and true thanks for your kind thoughts of me in my misery. Blessed Bobby was the light of my life and his love for me quite incomparable. So with his dear father's loss . . . you can believe how stricken I am . . . I hope Billy will come home and you have Una.*
>
> *Violet Dunville*

It is worth here spending a little time in reflecting on the life of Una's oldest brother, Bobby, who was an equally intriguing man as other members of the family. This again is an extract from the family website:

> *Robert Lambart Dunville, who like his brothers, had been educated at Eton, was commissioned into the Buckinghamshire Yeomanry in October 1914. In April 1915, a Medical Board at the Military Hospital in Cottonera, Malta, described how he had just recovered from an attack of acute appendicitis and recommended that he should return to England for an appendectomy.*

By September, he had fully recovered and in November, he transferred as a Lieutenant to the Fifth Reserve Battalion, Grenadier Guards. He was in Ireland when the rebellion broke out in Dublin in April 1916 and set off to join his regiment there. On the way he was captured in Castle Bellingham, County Louth, by Irish Republicans who thought he was a spy. They placed him against a wall and shot him, leaving him for dead. Although he survived, he never fully recovered from his wounds and died fifteen years later at the age of 38.

Robert's special interest was zoology. He collected wild animals from all over the world and kept them in a private zoo in the grounds of Redburn House. A high wall was built in 1920 to protect the circular area of the zoo. The best known of the animals was Bruno the tame bear. He learned to sit on some of the chain by which he was tethered, so that it looked shorter than it was. If he was teased by anyone, he would leap out to the full length of the chain to seek his revenge. Robert's father, John Dunville, sometimes took Bruno to the family house in Portland Place, London and let it loose in the house, much to the protests of Violet. Appropriately for Robert's love of animals, the memorial built for him near the gates of Redburn House by Violet was a horse trough, complete with a drinking fountain and a drinking basin for dogs. The animals from Robert's private zoo became the start of the collection of the Belfast Zoological Gardens, which were opened in 1934.

Unfortunately, records during the next ten years are sketchy. There are no further letters from Violet, although this doesn't mean to say that she didn't correspond with Normansfield or visit Una. However, there is no doubt that she was still reeling from the deaths of her husband and two sons. Her youngest son, William (Billy), was something of a disappointment to her. He had embarked on a marriage that did not meet with the approval of the family, and he and his wife were 'banished' to Australia to run the family's sheep farm at Barry Station in Nundle, New South Wales. The couple later returned to Northern Ireland and divorced. Soon afterwards William emigrated to Canada with his two daughters and died in 1956.

Violet continued to live at Redburn House until her death in 1940. In her will she left money to William and his family, friends, and to various hospitals and charities, including £500 for a fund to be known as the John Spencer Dunville, VC, Trust. This sum was to be invested and the income used to make a gift on each Armistice Day to ex-servicemen, their dependents or the poor of the Parish of Holywood. No bequeath was made to Normansfield, although there must have been some financial arrangement made for Una's fees to be paid whilst she remained at the hospital.

After Violet's death, Redburn House was commandeered by the Air Ministry to accommodate members of Women's Royal Air Force. Following the war, the house became derelict and vandalised, and it was later demolished. It was replaced first by a hotel and then eventually by Holywood Nursing Home. The land was used for a cemetery, a school, a housing estate and Redburn Country Park, which is now open to the public. In the 1950's, the buildings of the Royal Irish Distilleries were taken over by a tobacco firm, which eventually abandoned them during the Troubles of the 1970's. The Distillery Football Club outlived the distillery and changed its name in 1999 to Lisburn Distillery, named after the location of its home ground.

Una lived on at Normansfield until her death on 28th September 1958 from the effects of influenza and a duodenal ulcer. She had resided at the hospital through two world wars and had witnessed the end of the institution as a private enterprise, although it is fitting that it was still a Langdon Down, Norman, who was 'the informant' on her death certificate.

It is also somewhat paradoxical that Una, at the age of 55, had outlived all her immediate family.

CHAPTER FOURTEEN

A DISPUTATIOUS CHARACTER

Society is an insane asylum run by the inmates.

Erving Goffman, sociologist and writer (1922-1982)

I don't mind if you don't like my manners. I don't like 'em myself.
They're pretty bad. I grieve over them long winter evenings.

Philip Marlowe, 'The Big Sleep',
Raymond Chandler (1946)

I n June 1970, the retirement of medical superintendent, Norman Langdon Down, brought to an end the family's involvement at Normansfield. A dynastic reign that had lasted just over a century had closed. Normansfield would never be the same.

In that year, the hospital consisted of 227 beds for mentally handicapped patients and 100 full time carers. For the first six months cover was provided by a consultant from Leavesden Hospital, Dr Eric Shepherd, until a Consultant Psychiatrist in Mental Subnormality, Dr Terence Lawlor, was appointed.

To be brutally honest, Dr Lawlor was not the greatest appointment in the history of the NHS. Aged 53 at the time, he was a former schoolteacher who didn't graduate in medicine until he was 39. At the time of taking up the post he had, despite his title, comparatively little experience in the treatment of subnormality. Coincidentally, he had worked as a locum medical

From the White House to bleak house: the arrival of Dr Lawlor to Normansfield in 1970 brought about a drastic regime change and a period of great unhappiness for patients and staff alike.

assistant at Earlswood for eight months before becoming a locum GP and then taking up his post at Normansfield. The spell at Earlswood seems to be about the only thing that he and John Langdon Down had in common.

His character was described as complex. To some he appeared to be a caring doctor – there are examples of letters he wrote to family members of some of the patients which show a real concern for their peace of mind. Other relatives found him helpful, but this seemed to be when they weren't questioning his motives. They were also in compromised positions in that they were so grateful that their kith and kin, who they couldn't look after at home, were at least safe and secure.

However, most found him abrasive, abrupt and arrogant, and occasionally witnessed his volatile temper. He viewed with suspicion and resentment volunteers who showed enterprise or initiative to help patients and nurses. A charge nurse keen to implement new ideas was subjected to ridicule, sarcasm and was addressed patronisingly as 'professor' by Dr Lawlor.

Lawlor's leadership was universally described as 'authoritarian and incompetent' and he was suspended six years later in the middle of a high profile strike by nursing staff, by which time care of the patients was in some cases appalling, the hospital buildings were in state of some disrepair and the morale of the staff was at an all time low.

Following the 1974 reorganisation of the National Health Service, Normansfield was managed by the Kingston and Richmond Area Health Authority and the South West Thames Regional Health Authority and was described as a 'problem' hospital. Three years into his tenure, poor working relationships between Dr Lawlor, his medical colleagues and most of the nursing staff already existed.

There was a lack of adequate dental care, physiotherapy, speech therapy and occupational therapy for the patients and a real difficulty in the recruitment and retention of good calibre trained nurses. It was a nightmarish task for staff to care for patients in run down, badly maintained and dirty buildings.

These problems, combined with complex management structures and increased union activity within the NHS, resulted on 5th May 1976 in a strike by most of the nursing staff demanding the suspension of Dr Lawlor. This industrial action was unprecedented in the history of the National Health Service.

To some degree, however, Lawlor had inherited some of the problems. Even under the stewardship of Norman Langdon Down things were not all rosy and by the late 1960's there was already a need 'to improve care and amenities including use of volunteers.' A chief nursing officer first saw the hospital in 1969 and stated,

> It might have been better in retrospect, to have bulldozed the lot and sold the grounds and used the money for building a new hospital.

A Health Authority report in 1970 noted:

> Much of the accommodation is, by modern standards, quite unsuitable for the care of the increasingly dependent patients who now require hospital admission.

A start was made on a new programme: improvements to the boiler house and some repairs to the roof and toilet areas.

Two years later, the Hospital Advisory Service visited again and concluded that the north and south wings constituted a serious fire risk and were unsuitable for patient accommodation. Unfortunately the imminent reorganisation meant that no remedial action was taken.

In minutes from a meeting of parents and staff in 1973, a number of concerns were already being raised about Dr Lawlor's regime. A charge nurse suggested that nurses were frightened to talk for fear of getting into trouble with their superiors. Dr Clarke, a community based doctor with a special responsibility for 'mentally handicapped' children, was available to be seen by parents but was told that he could not act alone and could only make recommendations to Dr Lawlor.

Another major difficulty was the shortage and turnover of staff, many of whom did not speak English very well. Patients' clothes had been lost and even some medical equipment, such as callipers, was found to have been put on incorrectly.

At the same time, the long-standing tradition of good relations with patients' relatives dwindled. Two parents who sat on the committee of the League of Friends were even warned not to interfere with the running of the hospital.

Another had written several times to Dr Lawlor asking for details of the drugs administered to his child, but had never received a reply. In another case Dr Clarke had requested to see the medical notes of a particular child but was refused permission by Lawlor. One father asked, 'How does one communicate with Dr Lawlor?'

Parents were increasingly encouraged to do their children's washing and the staff also needed more parent involvement in the education unit.

Yet Dr Lawlor was apparently 'very wary' of the suggestion to set up a parents drop-in centre as he was apparently concerned about the families forming a pressure group. Despite his opposition, the support centre did open, next to the hydrotherapy centre and shop. It was run by volunteers and proved to be a valuable resource where relatives could meet and swap stories. Lawlor never came to terms with its existence – he simply viewed it as a place where relatives would congregate to make trouble and issue complaints.

As early as 1974, a report by Mr R J Wix, a principal nursing officer at Longrove Hospital in Surrey, said:

> The nursing staff at Normansfield would have appeared to have lost their way. They do not participate in any active programme by which patients can achieve their maximum potential and thus enrich their lives.

The Community Health Council reported that there was no therapy, patients were expected to sit for hours on end, the lockers held no personal possessions and that there was a total lack of stimulation. Members found amongst generally filthy conditions:

> One child lying naked and unattended on his bed, urinating on the floor and bellowing.

A further visit two years later was equally depressing:

> The place was dirty, uninspired, patients seemed resigned and without the spark of friendliness.

But still nothing changed – mainly because of the obduracy of Dr Lawlor. In response to criticism following an Organisation and

Management report, Lawlor wrote:

> *I have no intention of changing my ways and am prepared to do battle with the Area Health Authority and the Regional Health Authority if necessary.*

Letters from the London Metropolitan Archive show that personnel problems at Normansfield date back to 1972 when a report refers to an urgent need to recruit staff, especially at weekends. There was obviously a shortage of domestics, another nursing officer needed appointing, staff were not inducted properly and there were four adults residing on a ward meant only for children.

Dr Lawlor and nursing officer Daphne Truman quarrelled constantly and viewed each other with open hostility from the beginning of their troubled working relationship. There were reports of a fight in the hospital's staff social club when both served on the committee. A letter from Daphne Truman shows the antagonism between them:

> *Social Club*
>
> *5th Aug 1973*
>
> *Dear Dr Lawlor,*
>
> *In view of the incident which took place at the social club in the early hours of last Sat morning the committee feel they must draw your attention to rule 1.3. It has been reported to the committee that you appeared at the social club at 1.30am on the 4th Aug and created a disturbance. The committee meet on Mon 13th Aug at 8.30pm. Your attendance is requested in order to give you an opportunity to explain your behaviour. Failing your attendance we will have no alternative but to act on the info laid before.*
>
> *D A Truman, Secretary*

Dr Lawlor duly resigned from the social club in November 1973, 'to be effective from the date of my "suspension" i.e. 10th August.'

Not long after, Daphne Truman was forbidden by Lawlor to go on to the wards – an instruction that was slightly tricky for a nursing officer. Lawlor also refused to talk to her and when communicating with other staff referred to the nursing officer in the third person, even in her presence.

Although Dr Lawlor treated her with utter contempt, Daphne Truman was no Florence Nightingale. It appears that she actually enjoyed some of these battles and at the ensuing inquiry she was described as 'an unreliable witness'.

Dr Lawlor was also at odds with Mrs Skeath, matron of Bill House, Normansfield's holiday home in Selsey Bill. They clashed over matters such as pocket money, dietary requirements and the number of organised coach trips. The 'domineering' Mrs Skeath, in turn, was less than enamoured by the number of unaccompanied patients travelling to Selsey, the suitability of some of these patients and even some of the staff members. Mrs Skeath wrote:

> *I will not accept an untrained female on night duty paid 50 shillings per hour responsible for these two patients, and request they be replaced.*

Another note from Mrs Skeath observed that:

> *Boys arrived with no luggage and one had vomited all over himself.*

Fewer and fewer patients were also sent to the Bill House – such a source of joy to patients down the years – after Norman Langdon Down retired and this seems to be because Dr Lawlor decreed it was too cold to send the patients there.

The Friends of Normansfield also fell out with Lawlor. They had expressed their concerns long before the strike, including over the hydrotherapy pool which had fallen into disuse, and the fact that more responsibility was expected of the volunteers. Elspet Rix describes Lawlor as:

> *A bit creepy - he was quite obsessive and would often call in relatives if he found fault in their visiting habits.*

Elspet felt that conditions deteriorated soon after Lawlor was appointed. Her own daughter, Shelley, was never mistreated, but was dressed inappropriately and often in other patients' clothes.

Voluntary organiser, Patricia Mott, who was extremely well respected within the hospital, experienced a disastrous first meeting with Dr Lawlor. He was abrupt and unwelcoming and subjected her to intense questioning, commenting sarcastically on her answers. On the subject of volunteer recruitment, he shocked her by proclaiming:

> *We don't want any drug addicts, queers or 'News Of The World' reporters.*

Given the state of his hospital, it's no surprise he wanted to avoid prying journalists. Mrs Mott later got into trouble for contacting outside agencies without permission and thus breaking the rules of confidentiality – something she claimed she would do again were it in the patients' interests. Her line manager, hospital administrator, Vernon Cursley was described in the inquiry report as having acted, 'in awe of Dr Lawlor and in general succumbed to his personality and influence'.

Throughout 1975, and during the first few months of 1976, the resentment of the nursing staff increased as a result of Dr Lawlor's restrictive and dismissive attitudes. The last straw came in February 1976 when Patricia Mott tried to introduce the 'One to One' project, a scheme by which members of the public were invited to 'adopt' individual patients as friends. A meeting was arranged with nursing officers and a BBC reporter was invited.

Surprisingly, it was not the BBC presence to which Lawlor objected. He appeared more concerned whether he could trust the nursing officers not to divulge to the public and other officials what was happening at the hospital, and refused to attend if they were present. The disgruntled nursing officers acquiesced but took union advice in response. Soon a petition was written on 15th March signed by five nursing officers and 22 senior nursing staff at Normansfield:

> *We the undersigned object to the behaviour displayed by Dr Lawlor, Consultant Psychiatrist at Normansfield, in regard to the following specific points: Attitude, Harrassment [sic], Interference in Nursing duties, Objections regarding Union membership.*
>
> *And we fear that if appropriate action is not taken we may find ourselves unable to co-operate any further with Dr Lawlor.*

This was actually contrary to union rules as any action should have been discussed and approved at a special meeting of the branch. It demonstrates the strength of feeling at the time.

There was no adequate response from the health authorities and the feelings of resentment in the staff deepened. The attitude of the members of COHSE (Confederation of Health Service Employees) was one of understandable anger and impatience. A union branch meeting was called on 4th May and there were demands for another meeting if Dr Lawlor wasn't suspended.

The events overnight were extremely chaotic and even according the report, 'the picture is not fully accurate'. There was merely a suggestion for a strike at 2am the following morning and the membership were left uncertain whether this would be official or unofficial. There was however a clear decision to strike from 7am the following morning. Pickets appeared outside the hospital an hour before although one trained nurse per ward was allowed to cross the line and bread, milk and drugs were allowed to be delivered.

These nurses were, however, later withdrawn and in response, the health authority provided cover from their own staff. Some of these administrators were inevitably untrained and there was no doubt that some patients were at risk, particularly those in need of regular medication. There had been some thought that the threat to strike was a bluff. And although they didn't want to be seen as submitting to union pressure, fears for the patients' safety persuaded the authority to take action.

At midday, Lady Robson, chair of the regional health authority, directed that Dr Lawlor should be suspended until after the next RHA meeting on 12th May, and also called for an inquiry. It was another three hours before the staff of Normansfield were informed and the strike was finally called off after 3pm that day.

The inquiry into 'Staff morale and patient care at Normansfield Hospital and in particular the circumstances leading to the withdrawal of labour by staff at the hospital on 5th May 1976, the action taken to deal with the situation and to make recommendations thereon' opened on 8th November 1976. Unfortunately it was adjourned after six days owing to the withdrawal of Dr Lawlor and the medical member of the panel.

A new committee of inquiry under the chairmanship of Michael

Sherrard, QC, was appointed by the Secretary of State for Social Services, David Ennals. The committee now had the power to receive evidence on oath and to compel the attendance of witnesses. Dr Lawlor did testify to the reconstituted inquiry, and actually attended 51 days of evidence. The proceedings were to be held in public unless some 'grave and weighty reason' was shown otherwise. Members of the committee made a number of visits to Normansfield between February and April 1977 at which time the topography of the hospital was the following:

NORTH WING
A three storey mid Victorian ward in the main block with sixty beds for adult men.

SOUTH WING
Also in the main block, housing seventy women, some with physical disabilities.

CONIFERS
A Victorian House separate form the main block. Thirty women patients. Some elderly.

EAST WING
Modern single storey block, in which thirty 'severely handicapped' men lived.

WEST WING
The residents consisted of thirty children and adolescents, who were mainly 'severely and physically handicapped.

Initial impressions by the committee members were that, 'the hospital was, generally speaking, filthy'. There were broken windows, damaged plasterwork, exposed dangerous sharp edges, foodstuff left next to drains, toilets and bedpans badly stained. Soiled incontinent pads were left lying around for days on end. Furniture was dumped on the wards and there was rubbish everywhere. Apart from Conifers, the wards were bare and 'reminiscent of scenes from the workhouse'. Even the gardens were neglected and overgrown.

Mattresses did not fit the beds and there was a shortage of linen. There was no activity on the wards. Patients were left to sit in their

The beginning of the end for Normansfield? During Dr Lawlor's 'reign' the declining standards inside the hospital mirrored the general neglect and deterioration of the building itself

chairs for hours on end, sometimes simply staring at the television test card. The patients didn't go outside, even on fine days. (Lawlor later admitted that patients were sometimes locked in their wards for as long as five hours at a time.) The gym and the hydrotherapy pool were hardly used. Patients were dressed in a manner which was degrading and slovenly – some of the female patients even without underwear.

The final visit was made in May 1978 and it appears that there was very little improvement in the hospital's conditions. The committee of inquiry sat for 124 days and its report was published in November 1978.

According to *The Nursing Times*:

> *The exhaustive inquiry report into conditions at Normansfield rates as one of the most damning and depressing accounts of mental handicap care under the NHS care ever produced. While Terence Lawlor is indicted above all others, nurses, administrators and other*

> *medical staff are shown to have failed abysmally in the delivery of*
> *care. While a number of ward nurses were "excellent and did what*
> *they could to overcome obstacles to good nursing" and while some*
> *sisters and charge nurses "struggled valiantly to maintain standards*
> *they were overwhelmed by the odds."*

A number of nursing officers were singled out for criticism. One was described as 'not being fit to hold his present post'. It was recommended that several others should not be employed again in the service and the hospital administrator was also criticised for staying on the sidelines in the arguments between Dr Lawlor and the nurses.

But it was inevitably Dr Lawlor who bore the brunt of the blame and the report stated that he should be sacked immediately and that he should not be re-engaged in any capacity in the NHS:

> *Dr Lawlor made the worst of an already poor situation. He was*
> *hypercritical of the nurses and he adopted an enforced and*
> *obsessively protective attitude towards patients, whose lives he*
> *needlessly and harmfully restricted. His intolerant, abusive and*
> *tyrannical regime drove away from the hospital other medical staff,*
> *paramedical and ancillary staff, as well as talented teachers and*
> *others who tried to assist with patients.*

The patently insecure Dr Lawlor had always been inordinately haunted by the possibility of litigation arising from accidents. He forbade visits to zoos, which he thought were unsuitable for mentally handicapped patients, or areas where there were lakes or woods. There were no spontaneous outings and nursing staff were even forbidden from taking patients to the nearby Bushy Park without his agreement or vetting of the list. Even a visit to a sweetshop, which did not necessitate the crossing of a main road (itself a source of intense anxiety to him), needed his written approval each time. Whenever a report was published, describing incidents at other hospitals, his preoccupation with the possibility of an accident increased.

Trivial bumps scratches and knocks had to be reported as accidents and as the number of 'injuries' increased, Lawlor's criticism of nursing staff also demoralised staff morale further. By

1975 many key personnel had resigned as a result of Dr Lawlor's mistrust. In fact, almost all the medical and paramedical staff withdrew from the hospital because of their poor relationships with him. The physiotherapist, speech therapist, head of school and a number of doctors were amongst many driven away by Lawlor's attitude. He even declined to wish new staff 'Good morning' if they weren't under his jurisdiction. A ward sister who retired after 37 years service, fifteen of them at Normansfield, revealed:

> *Dr Lawlor would not discuss the patients with us and used to say,*
> *"I am the consultant psychiatrist and I make the decisions".*

Dr Lawlor even attempted to subject three overweight patients to a rigid diet of porridge-like substance for a month. He was convinced when they didn't lose weight that someone had been secretly providing them with sweets and he ordered them to be locked up together in a room, until the nurses protested. He also subjected patients to drug trials without their knowledge.

Lawlor was also shown to have a loose interpretation of the truth and was caught out again and again during his testimony at the inquiry. He misled his solicitors and counsel and presented his case to the national press that he had been a victim of trade union action because he had had the courage to complain that patients were victims of ill treatment at the hands of the nurses.

The only mitigation seems to be that Lawlor was inexperienced and he was certainly isolated. This was his first job as a Consultant. Normansfield was remote from other hospitals, and there were no other full time Consultants in post, denying him valuable peer group support. However, he compounded the situation by alienating any staff members by adopting procedures that suited him alone. He wasn't at all happy working in a multi-disciplinary setting. Maria Scott, a child psychologist, was employed for three sessions a week at the hospital but was forced to resign.

The Education Act 1970 handed local education authorities responsibility for the education of 'handicapped' children, including those previously considered unsuitable for education.

Richmond LEA took two rooms in the Stella Brain building and opened the school in September 1971. The imaginative head teacher, Priscilla Mills, was the unit's driving force. Like John Langdon Down she used music and drama as learning devices. Mrs Mills had a background in psychology, something that immediately made Lawlor suspicious. In fact, he warned her not to employ therapeutic theories on the children. This however didn't deter Mills:

> *All along the line I felt it was necessary to fight for better conditions at Normansfield ... I admit fully that at all times from when I took on my job until the point of resigning I never stopped fighting for what I thought was a very worthy cause.*

Priscilla Mills was, in fact, one of the few staff members to be praised by the findings of the inquiry. The report recorded:

Under a typical tabloid headline, The Daily Mail's coverage accuses the trade unions of putting their solidarity before the care of the patients.

*Her tact and tenacity are greatly to be applauded. We are in no
doubt about her skill ability and dedication.*

Unsuited by personality and temperament, Dr Lawlor was
consistently provocative towards other members of staff. He
inhibited, and in some instances, actually prevented the best care,
treatment and attention being given to the patients. It was even
reported at the inquiry that his drug prescribing practices were
open to serious criticism.

The press, of course, revelled in the scandal and *The Daily Mail*,
although critical of the nurses' industrial action, reported that:

> *Appalling conditions had existed for years. Patients had no privacy
> in the toilets because broken doors were not replaced. There were
> no curtains round the baths and showers. Many patients had no
> individual clothing. Demarcation disputes between nursing and
> domestic staff and between day and night nursing shifts contributed
> to excrement being left around for hours, sometimes days. The
> children's unit was so dirty one doctor remarked, "I did not feel
> there was a place I could put my handbag."*
>
> *An incontinent patient was scrubbed by a nursing assistant with
> a toilet brush and difficult patients were locked up in side rooms.
> Christmas decorations were left up for months. There were no
> regular planned activities for the patients.*

The Surrey Comet of 11th February summed up the scale of the
investigation:

> *Britain's longest and probably most costly public inquiry ended in
> London yesterday in a quiet room off Pall Mall. It had involved
> one hundred and forty five witnesses, more than eight million words
> of evidence and twenty four thousand pages of official transcripts
> and proceedings. The bill for the one hundred and twenty four day
> investigation into conditions at Normansfield Hospital is expected to
> exceed half a million pounds – most of it borne by the taxpayer.*

Following the inquiry, Terence Lawlor emigrated to Australia where,
according to Brian Rix, 'he continued to work as a psychiatrist with
his pension intact!'

REPORT OF THE COMMITTEE OF INQUIRY INTO NORMANSFIELD HOSPITAL

The report Presented by the Secretary of State for Social Services (David Ennals) by command of her Majesty November 1978.

The Report shows that the present system of consensus management in the NHS did not work effectively in respect of Normansfield Hospital.

I must make it clear that the sort of behaviour and the poor standards of care revealed at Normansfield must not be tolerated in our hospitals.

There were clearly some people at Normansfield whose concern for patients endured in spite of every difficulty. The difficulties must be overcome. A 'Task Force' consisting of senior nursing and administrative staff has been established to provide new leadership and to try to restore confidence at the hospital.

PRINCIPAL CONCLUSIONS

The quality of life of the patients at Normansfield Hospital during the past six years at least has been impaired by a failure of the senior medical, nursing and administrative officers in post to co-operate with each other in the delivery of care. This failure was compounded by the Area Health Authority.

Hostility between Dr Terence Lawlor on the one hand and virtually all the other nursing, paramedical and ancillary services on the other was the principal factor giving rise to the troubles at the hospital.

There is with one exception, no evidence whatsoever of cruelty or ill treatment of patients by members of the nursing staff. The exceptional case was one of thoughtless rough handling by a nursing assistant.

The standard of nursing care was generally low and the quality of life of many of the patients suffered accordingly. Shortage of staff at different levels was at various times a contributory factor, but it was by no means the principal cause of difficulty. The Senior Nursing Officer was weak and ineffectual and failed to display the necessary determination and leadership vital to the proper discharge of his duty to the patients.

For long periods of time the hospital buildings were neglected and dangerous. They had a patchwork quilt of makeshift repair and poor workmanship. The roof of the building let in water for many years and the upper floor had to be evacuated because rain water poured in and it was feared that the ceiling would collapse. Patients were sometimes soaked as they slept. The standards of hygiene were often appalling and patients and staff alike suffered from demarcation disputes between nursing and domestic staff. Faeces and urine were frequently left unattended for days on end.

Dr Lawlor made the very worst of an already poor situation. He was hypercritical of the nurses and he adopted and enforced an obsessively protective attitude towards patients whose lives he needlessly and harmfully restricted. He was fettered by his fear of personal censure and of being held responsible for any and every untoward occurrence. His intolerant, abusive and tyrannical regime drove away from the hospital and other medical staff, para- medical and ancillary staff as well as talented teachers and others who tried to assist with patients. Initiatives designed to improve the quality of life of the patients were stifled and opportunities for progress were lost.

The creation of this isolated post was a fundamental error aggravated by Dr Lawlor's personality. No cover was provided – his own sense of isolation increased.

Although well meaning, the administrator lacked initiative and drive and succumbed to Lawlor's authority of whom he was afraid.

When the new Health Authority took over Normansfield on the reorganisation of the Health Service in April 1974, it was already run down and experiencing difficulties.

We applaud the single-handed attempt of the teacher in charge of the Local Education Authority School, Mrs Priscilla Mills, to bring to the attention of the authorities the plight of her children under her educational care. She fought Dr Lawlor with tact and determination and retired, exhausted, from the scene, only when she had won for the children the rights to which they were entitled.

The strike might well have been avoided had the Health Authority reacted with promptness during the six weeks preceding. By the 19th March 1976, a petition from the hospital's nursing staff relating to their grievances with regard to Dr Lawlor had been received by Area officers. Between 20th March and the strike on

5th May, no Area Officer took any steps to meet the nurses to discuss fundamental complaints. No one went to Normansfield for the purpose. The Senior Officer abdicated his role and effectively with drew from his managerial role.

The staff at Normansfield were convinced that nothing short of drastic action on their part could produce the result they wanted by the end of April, namely to be rid of Dr Lawlor.

The Area Nursing Officer reported that the patients were in serious danger by mid-day on the 5th May 1976 and feared an accident might occur. However, it was not until about one o'clock that afternoon that the Regional Team Officer recommended to the chairman of the Regional health Authority, Lady Robson of Kiddington that Dr Lawlor should be suspended. Despite the knowledge that patients were in peril the decision to suspend Dr Lawlor was not notified to the staff at Normansfield until 3.30 pm that afternoon, whereupon they returned to the wards. An unnecessary and dangerous delay of at least two hours was involved.

CHAPTER FIFTEEN

"IS HE ONE OF THOSE PLASTIC BABIES?"

There's no such thing as a wrong note.

Art Tatum, jazz pianist (1909-56)

When Gordon Bairnsfather was born in Willesden, London in 1951, one of his first introductions to the outside world at the age of six weeks was a trip to the local baby clinic. Following a cursory inspection of the baby and an affirmation that Gordon did indeed have Down's syndrome, the doctor shrugged her shoulders and said, 'don't worry, there are places for children like these. In any case, they don't live long.' Gordon's mother, Jessica Merrilees, at the time of our interview an extraordinarily feisty 92 year old, recalls:

> *If I hadn't picked Gordon up straightaway and taken him out of there, I would have slapped the woman.*

It would be fair to say that this particular medical practitioner didn't know quite who she was dealing with. Jessica describes herself as 'a fighter', who through circumstances of birth had always had to battle for her rights.

Gordon's father, John Bairnsfather, who played trombone under the name of Jock Bain with some of the biggest dance bands of the day (including Roy Fox and his Orchestra and Billy Cotton's band) took one look at Gordon and simply announced that, 'He can't be my baby'.

That was the final straw for Jessica who had endured Jock's womanising, drinking and violence. She threw him out, initiating a very messy separation. She already had two children, Roger and Jane, to care for and life would now be precarious. Jock's cruel words, however, had left her no option.

Jessica's background provided her with the determination and confidence to cope. Born at the start of the First World War, Jessica didn't even see her father until she was six years old. She was the oldest of nine siblings and was given the responsibility of looking after the younger children. She married Jock at the age of eighteen and left her home city of Edinburgh to live in London, where she and her musician husband experienced a bohemian existence.

As soon as Gordon was born and lay across her body, Jessica knew that, 'he was a Mongol'. She had encountered other children like Gordon, although in those days, they were kept apart from everyone else and mainly institutionalised. Jessica knew that no matter what, 'That wasn't going to happen to my Gordon'.

She immediately sought out information about 'Mongolism' and literally tramped the streets, but without success. With Jock still refusing to have anything to do with their son (despite the fact that Jessica thought they looked exactly alike), and in the face of a complete lack of factual material, Jessica took charge of the situation.

She made contact with other parents of disabled children and formed a group called the Parents of Backward Children, which was actually the forerunner of Mencap (launched in 1946). This group would not only provide support for other isolated parents but also helped with fundraising and even initiated a day centre for the children. Jessica had achieved a certificate for childcare in Scotland and later opened a nursery catering for 'handicapped' children.

Although Gordon's care now dominated her life (resulting in her decision to send her older son, Roger, to boarding school), Jessica never felt resentful. She did know, however, that life would always be difficult for Gordon and that he would never be able to achieve much because of the restraints that society of the time would place on him.

In the years after the war (and right up to 1970) there was no formal schooling for children with disabilities and even reading and writing was not encouraged. Jessica now regrets the fact that she didn't ensure that Gordon received even these basic tenets of education.

Back then, very few 'Mongol' children were seen in the community and Jessica had to suffer the torment of insensitive remarks from ignorant strangers. Public perception was skewed by the prominent publicity and fundraising by the Spastics Society (a charity specifically for people with the neurological disability cerebral palsy) there was a common belief that any handicapped baby must be 'spastic'. In the early 1950's, Jessica made a trip to Sainsbury's and left Gordon in his pram outside the shop. On her return, she discovered a gaggle of women huddled round Gordon. One woman peered into the pram, gave Jessica a pitying look and asked, 'Is that one of those plastic babies?'

Unbelievably, soon after, another woman studied this very white, tiny baby and said, 'You know why you've got a Mongol baby? It's all these blacks coming into the country'!

Some things never change: the day after my wife, Alison, gave birth to our daughter, Sarah, in 1992 she was warned by a hospital domestic that Sarah's Down's syndrome must have been caused by Allie smoking too many drugs during pregnancy! Another nursing assistant later asserted that because Allie had worked as a hospital social worker, she had listened to too many peoples' problems, and 'it's rubbed off on your baby'.

However, a few years after Gordon's birth, Jessica eventually discovered a local National Health day centre which he could attend. Jessica was able to find employment and she worked as an assistant to the 'almoner' (social worker) at the Marie Curie Hospital in Hampstead. Later Jessica was employed as a social worker working with physically handicapped children. She arranged for a friend to look after Gordon when he returned home from the centre so that she could work full time.

When Gordon was ten years old, Jessica herself needed hospital treatment. There was no one who could care for Gordon on a full time basis and she was advised by her GP to contact Norman Langdon Down, then medical superintendent at Normansfield. She immediately warmed to 'Dr Norman' and felt she could entrust her son to his care. Gordon stayed for three weeks while Jessica was laid up and she was amazed how well he settled in.

The staff were 'marvellous' and Dr Langdon Down assured her that if she ever needed respite care for Gordon she could contact him direct – 'You don't need to go via your GP, just give me a ring'. Although the hospital was now under the auspices of the NHS, Jessica was surprised that she was never charged for these respite stays and was always grateful for this invaluable help.

Despite the fact that Jessica had always maintained she didn't want Gordon to be institutionalised, she realised that he began to enjoy his time at Normansfield more and more and was benefiting from the companionship of other children like him – 'Gordon's life at Normansfield was more than I could give him'. As soon as they reached the gates of the hospital Gordon couldn't wait to enter the grounds and would say excitedly, 'Boys now! Bye mum!'

Several years later, she and Gordon discussed his future and together they came to the decision that he would move to Normansfield permanently. Jessica was naturally deeply upset but felt that Gordon would be happy there and well looked after. It was, however, a terrible realisation that she 'didn't matter anymore'.

Gordon was admitted to Trematon in 1964 and he immediately struck up relationships with other residents. He became friends with Shelley Rix, who called him 'Popeye' because he used to carry around a Popeye doll. Gordon never liked his nickname although it stuck with him for more than 40 years!

Jessica describes Normansfield at that time as 'a large private home, full of children from different backgrounds'. Gordon enjoyed good health and was a popular boy, friendly and cheerful. He also liked going on holiday to the Bill House holiday home in Selsey Bill, which was owned by Normansfield.

Jessica, who was now a qualified social worker and was working full time with homeless families in Hackney, visited him every Saturday, usually taking him to tea at Bentalls department store in nearby Kingston.

The situation changed dramatically, however, with the appointment of Dr Terence Lawlor. Norman Langdon Down had been something of a father figure to patients and staff alike but with the arrival of Lawlor, Jessica felt that 'the staff were lost souls'. Jessica describes Lawlor as inept and unable to cope with his responsibilities. They soon clashed. Gordon was admitted to hospital but Jessica wasn't actually informed until she was about to visit him: she received a phone call from a member of staff advising her not to come.

It subsequently transpired that a nurse wielding a shoe had hit her son on the head – an episode Jessica only learned about when Gordon told her. Jessica confronted Dr Lawlor and the incident was reported to the police. The nurse subsequently disappeared but was never charged with any criminal offence.

Jessica felt that the standard of care at Normansfield went rapidly downhill during the 1970's. She could never get any answers to her ever more frequent complaints, the facilities deteriorated and she described some of the buildings as filthy. Whereas previously there had been very little communication between parents, they now started to talk to each other and to meet regularly to exchange notes and discuss the situation. Jessica felt the place was going to rack and ruin and it was no surprise to her when the staff went on strike to oust Dr Lawlor.

Following Lawlor's suspension, Jessica gave evidence to the committee of inquiry, which was reported in *The Daily Mail* on 5th September 1977. Under the headline *FEAR OF A MOTHER WHO KNEW*, it states that Jessica Merrilees told the inquiry:

> *If you have any worries or anxieties which you would like to discuss it is generally impossible to do so and this can make you feel very frustrated.*

The article continues:

> *Mrs Merrilees was asked why she did not make more inquiries to which she replied, "Well after many years of having my son in an institution, I feel, as I sit here today and say this to you, that I too have become institutionalised. It is all very well to say, why didn't you do this, why didn't you do that, but you become so depressed . . . there is a sort of paralysis that sets in because you are unable to keep pushing at these things because the distress is so much to bear."*

Jessica recalls one time arriving unexpectedly at Normansfield – something she never normally did for fear of what she might see. She found Gordon in an ancient pair of trousers that were torn from the crotch to the knee:

He would have been indecently exposed if it weren't for a pair of pants underneath. It brought to the surface all my feelings about having a son who can't care for himself and I created quite a scene with the nurse. That got me nowhere. All that happened was that they made excuses about keeping the best clothing locked away to protect it.

Jessica reaffirmed that when Gordon first went to Normansfield,

. . . there had existed a lovely atmosphere and it was a very happy place, but morale began to break down in the last few years.

Once Dr Lawlor was out of the picture, Jessica acknowledges that the general care at the hospital improved again. Gordon loved participating in Wolfgang Stange's dance sessions and performances and she and Gordon both enjoyed the annual sports day, especially the tug of war competition between relatives and staff. Jessica also used to run a cake stall at the Christmas fair.

She was also impressed with the Stella Brain School which she described as very successful, providing both education and stimulation for the children.

Gordon (right) with friend at one of Wolfgang Stange's drama sessions.

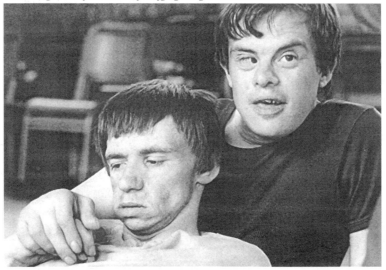

When the closure of Normansfield was first discussed in the mid 1980's, Jessica was naturally concerned about Gordon's future. Her fears were soon justified. Everything, she says, was in a muddle. Some of Gordon's friends moved into a Mencap house and she was disappointed that there seemed to be no plans to keep together people who had formed close relationships over many years in the hospital.

Gordon was moved into the 'halfway house' in Kingston Road, at the edge of the hospital grounds. Jessica recalls that there was absolutely no assistance provided with the move and she and Gordon themselves had to transport his furniture in. People who had been institutionalised for decades were suddenly left mainly to fend for themselves. The only staff at Kingston Road were two women who were not nurses and had no experience with learning disabled. They were on duty from 9am to 5pm, but no member of night staff was engaged. When Gordon became ill on one occasion Jessica had to sleep in a chair for three nights in his tiny room to keep an eye on him. Worryingly, Gordon was also sharing the house with a man who had been known to be violent.

Gordon remained in this 'temporary accommodation' for nearly 20 years until he was transferred in 2004 to the newly built residential home in the Normansfield grounds.

At the time of writing, Gordon is now extremely settled in the residential home and enjoys listening to music and watching musicals. He is extremely sociable and attends two day centres. His two siblings, who have always understood the reasons for Gordon's admission to Normansfield, visit regularly and are a great deal of support to him and their mother.

In September 2006, Jessica and Gordon attended a reunion of patients and relatives at Normansfield. A string quartet had been hired to add the atmosphere of a tea dance and Jessica was cheered that Gordon was so clearly delighted to be back in the theatre where he had attended classes and performed regularly.

Despite her physical frailty, Jessica remains a wonderfully strong and assured woman. She has never viewed Gordon as 'a victim' of Down's syndrome. She reserves her anger for a society that has victimised her son:

You see, it is attitudes that are the real disability.

CHAPTER SIXTEEN

A BEAUTY
OF THEIR OWN

Movement never lies. It is a barometer telling the state
of the soul's weather to all who can read it.

Martha Graham, pioneer of modern dance
(1894-1991)

T his chapter is the story of a remarkable man, who inspired patients at Normansfield with his dedication, imagination and determination for nearly fifteen years. A man, supported by a few devoted helpers, who unceasingly fought the bureaucracy and obduracy of the institution's hierarchy.

Wolfgang Stange, a native Berliner, is a dancer, teacher and choreographer, who each Tuesday from 1975 onwards ran a dance and drama session for the hospital patients. Every patient, no matter how disabled, was welcomed into the group and given the opportunity to perform.

Originally trained at the London School of Contemporary Dance, Wolfgang describes his initial involvement of working with the learning disabled initially as an 'accident', although others might call it serendipity. During his final year of training Wolfgang was asked by an enlightened occupational therapist student to do some voluntary work at Springfield Psychiatric Hospital in south London. Wolfgang was initially reluctant:

> *I really didn't want to do it, she just asked me to come. So I*
> *explained how I had a few ideas, how I would love to share my*

love for dance with the people and they accepted that and let me
work there, once a week on a daily basis.

At Springfield, one of the patients drew his attention to an advertisement asking for people to work in a hospital for the learning disabled. Wolfgang felt that he lacked the experience for such a post and so couldn't apply for the job. He did, however, mention this to one of his teachers and it transpired that she was a friend of Gina Levete, the person who had actually placed the advert . . .

Gina Levete MBE, a mime artist, had founded a community-based company called 'Shape', whose founding principle was to provide access to the arts for deaf and disabled people. Wolfgang contacted her.

George Beven's oil painting of Wolfgang Stange. Originally trained at the London School of Contemporary Dance, from 1975 Wolfgang ran dance and drama sessions for the patients at Normansfield irrespective of the level of their disability. He also fought against the bureaucracy and obduracy of the institution's hierarchy.

*She listened to what I had to say about my work and just asked if
I would I like to work with the mentally handicapped. I said that
my philosophy, the way I was teaching, should not be limited to
one group in particular – it should embrace anyone who wishes to
dance. Gina asked me if I'd like to have a go and told me about
this place called Normansfield, who really wanted someone to teach
the staff to do creative movement.*

This was actually Wolfgang's first professional engagement; he
was paid the princely sum of £3.50 per session. He went to
Normansfield for two hours each week and was originally allocated
about 20 residents to work with, most of whom had Down's
syndrome. Apart from a voluntary organiser and excellent support
from the school in the form of costumes, Wolfgang was left alone
to get on with his work – no extra members of staff were provided
to assist him.

*I had of course no experience in a sense, except for me wanting to
show my love of dance to people who had limited access to it.*

Gina Levete attempted, unsuccessfully, to obtain regular assistance
for Wolfgang, not just for the patients' benefit but also to provide
him with some professional protection should anything go wrong,
but without success. It didn't deter Wolfgang:

*Occasionally we used to get the odd nurse coming in, one or two
who really wanted to do it and then couldn't come back because
duty wouldn't allow them to. Some I preferred not to have in the
class because they were utterly negative!*

Some parents and relatives backed his initiative but staff largely
thought he was wasting theirs and the patients' time. Wolfgang was
delighted to work in the Grade 2-listed theatre and made sure that
he made full use of this unusual space. His first production in 1975
was a nativity play, as he felt the Christmas story was one that most
of the residents would already have known and understood.

On the basis of that success, Wolfgang became more ambitious,
devising an original piece called *The Friendship Journey*. It was a story
about love and understanding, based, again, around Christ's birth.

Wolfgang introduced some Japanese and Indian music and hired two professional American actors to supplement the cast.

The staff magazine of the Kingston and Richmond Area Health Authority of July 1977 wrote a glowing review:

THE FRIENDSHIP JOURNEY

by Wolfgang Stange

Wolfgang Stange is a dancer and creative movement therapist supported by Shape, an organisation backed both by Leverhulme Trust and the Gulbenkian Foundation. He has been working with about twenty residents at Normansfield for nearly two years now, improving their physical skills and channelling these achievements into shows. The most recent was 'The Friendship Journey' put on at Normansfield on 9th June before a mixed audience of parents, staff, volunteers and outside groups of the mentally-handicapped.

'The Friendship Journey', performed almost entirely by residents, is aimed to put over a message of love between all individual human beings by telling of the adventures of a group of people travelling through different lands and the welcoming acceptance of the group by the local inhabitants. This theme was suggested in dance form set to music from Ceylon, Japan and Africa, and to music representing journeys by rail, sea and air. The reception the performance received indicated that it was an unqualified success; yet it was more than just a success as a show.

Comments voiced by several professional dancers in the audience confirmed that Wolfgang's work has wrought a remarkable change in the performers' physical abilities, in their ease of movement and skill in expressing themselves through movement. To this Wolfgang has added that he has observed personality changes for the better and a genuine group spirit developing which has included those who were regarded as 'loners'. Bearing this in mind it seems evident that, although the finer points of the action may not have come across to all, the essential message of the 'Journey' did, to both performers and their counterparts in the audience.

Not for the first time, Normansfield was setting trends in care for the learning disabled, with or without wholehearted staff support.

Wolfgang had a variety of patients with a range of disabilities attending his sessions. Sophie, a young woman with Down's syndrome, regularly came to Wolfgang's classes but refused to participate and would sit under the piano. Every Tuesday, Wolfgang would invite her to join the group, but she wouldn't respond. Some of the nursing staff thought it was ridiculous that Wolfgang pursued her participation and they even actively discouraged her attendance. He was even summoned to a meeting with an angry administrator who insisted that Sophie be withdrawn. Wolfgang was equally resolute that she be given the opportunity to be with the group, insisting that the young woman must be benefiting in some way from the sessions:

> *I told him, If she didn't get something out of it she wouldn't have come into the room every week.*

For eighteen months, Sophie sat under the piano, ignoring Wolfgang's imperturbable requests. He even moved the group right next to the piano, so as to include her.

Eventually, one memorable day, Sophie actually pointed to the tea tray and indicated that she wanted some tea. Taken aback, Wolfgang responded coolly, saying, 'I'm not your slave, get it yourself'.

To everyone's amazement, Sophie did just that – only to retreat back to the safety of the piano. However, this was the breakthrough that Wolfgang had been waiting for and Sophie gradually involved herself in the sessions, eventually participating regularly. Wolfgang had been convinced that Sophie was making a commitment to the group just by being in the room – a conviction that was proved right.

The dignity of each patient was paramount in Wolfgang's philosophy at Normansfield, no matter what the manifestation of disability. There was one autistic resident in his group who was obsessed by water and nursing staff had warned Wolfgang that the man should be accompanied to the toilet at all times. Wolfgang felt that this was demeaning to treat an adult in this way and refused this advice, allowing the patient to go on his own to the lavatory. Unfortunately, the next thing the group heard was a huge crash followed by the sound of gushing water. The basin had been removed and there was quite a flood.

There was much recrimination and told-you-sos from the staff members, but Wolfgang felt that he had to give his charge an opportunity to be independent. From then on, however, he was always on the lookout for future incidents and ready to make a dash for the toilet . . . just in case.

Penny, another dance class member with autism, would sit hunched in a chair, arms crossed, showing no sign of interest or involvement. After some months of this behaviour even Wolfgang's patience was being tried and so he kneeled at her feet asking her, 'What am I doing with you? Am I wasting my time? What is the point of this?'

After a pause, Penny reached out, smiled and gently stroked his face. From this affectionate and positive gesture, Wolfgang knew she was completely engaged in the group. It confirmed the importance of working at the pace of the individual and reinforced Wolfgang's belief that these classes were all about the students, not the frustrations of his own teaching.

David, who had both physical and learning disabilities, was extraordinarily graceful, but needed constant reassurance from his teacher. Wolfgang gave him a prop – a cassette tape case and told David, 'Now I want you to look at this only when you dance, don't look at me!'

Every time he tried to ask Wolfgang something, David was told to look at the case. This displacement method took a few weeks to be effective, as Wolfgang explains:

> I had to keep it up for quite a few weeks. I wanted him to find his own focus, which later he didn't need any more. He had a total inner focus when he danced. He looked beautiful. He did not ask any more because he knew it was right and that was very clear.

Wolfgang also took ideas from his students and was always open to discovering new ways of maintaining the patients' focus:

> Sally was very gifted. Always she would know instinctively what a line was. She would create lines. I didn't have to teach her, it was just inborn. We had our little fights, she could be very stubborn. She wanted to dance her way. I told her that I respected what she did, but that I wanted her to do different things. I had to really

push hard then not for her to fall back and repeat the things she had been praised for before. But she was very, very talented, one of my best dancers in the group . . . very artistic.

Wolfgang inevitably experienced some friction with Dr Terence Lawlor, although, on the whole, the Consultant Psychiatrist who ran Normansfield stayed well clear of the dance teacher. (Not quite his thing.) One encounter, however, is recounted by Wolfgang and demonstrates Lawlor's attitude:

One day I was doing something on stage and he came in and stood there at the back wearing his white coat. I just carried on because Lawlor didn't introduce himself. So after ten minutes I said, "Excuse me, can I help you?" He shouted at me and gesticulated to one of the group: "What is Meredith doing here?" So I said, "Well, what is your interest?" He asked me if I knew what medication the patient was on and I replied no. Lawlor said that he should not be under the lights because they could cause problems. I said I was awfully sorry, but it didn't seem to cause any ill effects. He just shouted at me and then walked out. He had still not introduced himself.

The following week, Wolfgang was summoned to the Consultant's office. Lawlor politely explained that a number of the patients were very ill and couldn't do 'these ballet things'. Wolfgang replied that he was not a magician and couldn't make ballet dancers of them, but that he was 'just showing them some other things'. He added that he understood the doctor's concern for his patients but that as he had not attended any of the sessions, he might perhaps 'be kind enough to come and see'. If, after that, Lawlor still felt that the patients were suffering, then he would accept what he was saying.

Unsurprisingly, Lawlor never did observe another of Wolfgang's sessions. Neither did he ever attend any of their shows. In fact, there was so much concern about his negativity towards them that one of the voluntary workers told Wolfgang that she was concerned Lawlor would sabotage the productions by arranging the patients to be over-medicated. This never happened and was probably over the top, but it speaks volumes of the atmosphere at the time.

Wolfgang was asked to give evidence at the inquiry into Normansfield in 1977, and as a result the entire judicial committee attended a performance to celebrate the Queen's Jubilee, much to Wolfgang's surprise:

> *It was the shock of my life. That was the first time ever we had such high positioned people in the audience. Never again after that did anybody come, but never mind they came for that.*

Even after the departure of Lawlor, Wolfgang still battled the hospital administration:

> *One day I came to my class and all my students had gone, nobody was there. Nobody had even bothered to inform me the previous week. There was a new occupational therapist who hadn't even told me that the patients had been sent to different units to do their work.*

The ubiquitous Heather Cadbury, who had been a nurse at the hospital and subsequently worked with Wolfgang as a volunteer, explained that following the opening of a new activity centre, Wolfgang lost all his students and he started to work with the more severely disabled:

> *His new group included people needing wheelchairs and those who had very little concentration or communication skills. Some wandered aimlessly around the hall, others sat rocking in corners . . . each week Wolfgang arrived with new ideas and materials from different countries, determined to use his creative skills. He actively encouraged them to experience a range of emotions and to express their feelings.*

Wolfgang explained that with the more disabled students, he found it 'offensive to push them into something – like taking their hands and clapping for them'. He felt he had to encourage and help them, but only for a certain amount of time:

> *I felt that for people with a limited experience, that they have their own movement patterns which have a beauty of their own.*

Wolfgang showed that he appreciated their pattern and actually copied them so that he himself could experience their movement:

I would sit alongside and put my hands next to them. Suddenly they had two hands or fingers moving, and then when I put the music on, I realised this was an art form in itself. It was a new movement discovery for me as a choreographer.

But even before the composition of his group had become more challenging, Wolfgang faced difficulties that would reduce even the most experienced director to tears. The first performance using patients and performers from outside the institution took place at Normansfield and was repeated for four days at the London Drama Centre in Chalk Farm. It was the group's first venture away from the hospital and due to the unpredictable nature of institutional life, Wolfgang would sometimes get on the bus with his most able performers missing and patients he had never seen in his life climbing aboard. Wolfgang also intended to take a group to the Commonwealth Institute, where there was an exhibition from Sri Lanka. In preparation, he showed them a globe of the world. Very few of the patients knew what it was or could even say the word, but Wolfgang pointed out where England and Sri Lanka were situated.

One of the male nurses, who had been standing in the corner watching this session, suddenly lost his temper, shouting, "How the fucking hell do they know what a fucking globe is!" He stormed out and slammed the door behind him. The nurse was unaware that Wolfgang's group was to form a circle, a globe of their own, to show that the world is made up of all types of people.

Three weeks later the group went to the Commonwealth Institute to explore the exhibition and then attended a lecture on Kenyan dance. Soon after the start, one of the patients, Graham, started to rock in his seat. The rocking backwards and forwards became more violent and Wolfgang was worried why he had become so upset. He was on the verge of removing him, when Graham jumped up, ran across the floor and as the lecturer leapt aside for safety, Graham hurried to a table, pointed and slowly said, "G…l…o…b…e…" There, on the table, was an enormous globe. Graham returned to his seat and was immediately calm. Wolfgang was shocked but incredibly moved. He felt that the only way Graham could explain his recognition and understanding of the globe was by a physical demonstration.

*He knew what it was and wanted to tell everybody. But I had not
in my wildest dreams thought that Graham had understood the
concept of the globe. Graham looked so bizarre, he was very uptight
and tense all the time, there was actually much more to him than
his appearance suggested, but nobody ever bothered to find out.
I will never forget about his trousers, which were about five sizes too
large and he constantly had to hold up. I had so many fights over
him, I used to take him back to the nurses and ask for him to be
changed so many times, and they hated me. He died about a year
after that.*

It was a tradition of Wolfgang's that, following a performance at
Normansfield, the cast and all those connected with the show
would come from backstage and share coffee and tea with the
audience. About a week after one production Wolfgang received a
bill for nearly £80 for tea and biscuits. He went to the catering
manager and said she must be mistaken. Picture the scenes:

CATERING MANAGER'S OFFICE

Catering manager: *I was told to bill you because you ordered it.*

Wolfgang: *You know when I have my students in London I
always pay for their tea and coffee, I don't mind paying for it, but
to pay for all their aunties and uncles. I draw the line here!*

Catering manager: *'Yes, but you ordered it, so you must pay!'*

*EXIT WOLFGANG, WHO ENTERS THE
ADMINISTRATOR'S OFFICE:*

Wolfgang: *This is the last straw!*

Administrator: *Why are you so excited?*

Wolfgang: *I have just been presented with this bill!*

Administrator: *Well you shouldn't have ordered it.*

Wolfgang: *I did not order it, I requested it. I said, "Could I
please have tea and coffee?" Nobody told me I had to pay for it.
If they had told me I had to pay for it I wouldn't have ordered it.'*

Administrator: *Well I am sorry.*

Wolfgang: *Okay, well I am paying this bill, but I am going to charge you for all the overtime I did here which I never charged a penny for. All the Saturdays I worked, all the extra rehearsals we did here. And let me tell you, I would charge not the Normansfield rates, but my London prices.*

EXIT STAGE LEFT.

TWO HOURS LATER. ENTER THE ADMINISTRATOR.

Administrator: *We'll pay this time!*

Wolfgang: *'Thank you.'*

THE END

Besides Heather Cadbury, Wolfgang received sterling support from Carol Rentoul, a ballet dancer and teacher, who had some years before worked in Egypt with a boy who had Down's syndrome and had developed an interest in adults and children with special needs. Carol arrived at time when Wolfgang was very dispirited and her involvement was so timely that he later referred to her as his Nureyev, because 'Fonteyn would have given up if Nureyev hadn't turned up.'

Carol went on to work at Normansfield one day a week for eight years during the 1980's, and remembers his dedication:

> *The classes were very creative and imaginative despite some of the misgivings of the staff with whom Wolfgang would often clash. He wouldn't stand any nonsense. Anyone that entered into the room would have to play some part – so reluctant staff members would find themselves playing trees.*

Carol described the choreography as often quite complex and the music at times was equally enigmatic. Apart from folk and world music, classical and opera, they also used the work of contemporary composers such as Stockhausen in their interpretative routines:

> *We danced with residents by holding their arms and allowing them to feel how the music made us dance. Their faces slowly relaxed and one could feel their tensions drifting away . . . we allowed them to express themselves in any way possible.*

Above: Dance teacher, Carol Rentoul with student. Opposite: Holding their lines – a study in concentration.

Wolfgang, Carol and dancers.

Wolfgang's philosophy at Normansfield was to create a safe environment for self-expression, allowing residents to be themselves and to be accepted for who they were; to experience their own spirit, their own greatness. Each individual had something to offer and he was insistent that the creativity of dance had to affect the day to day lives of the patients:

> *Anyone can dance, no matter how disabled, because dance is movement. If you just express yourself by moving your head or your fingers or any part that you can move then that is dance for me. Rather than me thinking I have to teach them the foxtrot, I have to think what we can both learn. That is the point, not to make them into something like I am or somebody else. That is not my teaching. I don't like to do that.*

Wolfgang is now a world-renowned dance teacher as well as being director of the acclaimed Amici Dance Theatre Company: a totally integrated dance troupe of disabled and able-bodied performers. He says he is still learning, has no regrets about not being 'in the mainstream' and has felt extremely privileged to work with disabled performers.

Wolfgang's work at Normansfield has been immortalised in a BBC film entitled, *Feel Free*, written by Nick Darke and broadcast in 1982 in which Ben Kingsley, sorry . . . Sir Ben Kingsley (a patron of Amici) played Wolfgang. Wolfgang was delighted with the idea, but understandably unhappy that the BBC insisted that they used non-disabled actors in place of the patients. The actors did, at least, familiarise themselves with the residents and attended sessions at the hospital.

In an institution that has employed its fair share of pioneers, Wolfgang was arguably one of the most inspiring and undoubtedly the hospital's most rebellious. As I finished my interview, he was settling down to write a report for the London Borough of Hammersmith and Fulham concerning Amici. Still railing against bureaucracy, he was just about to pen a fictitious paragraph, describing how he used his disabled dancers as targets in a knife throwing act, 'Just to see if they actually bother to read these reports properly.'

CHAPTER SEVENTEEN

BEHIND THE WALL

"There must be some way out of here," said the joker to the thief,
"There's too much confusion, I can't get no relief."

'All Along The Watchtower'
Words & music by Bob Dylan

On 28th June 1990 a Dutch teenager, Miriam Bruinsma, left the Netherlands on a journey that was to have a dramatic effect on her life. With her belongings crammed into a small rucksack, she arrived in England to commence her working life at Normansfield. Employed as a care assistant between 1990 and 1993, this is Miriam's personal account of her time at the hospital in a period of great change:

> *I call this 'behind the wall' because someone I have been in contact with through my website coined the phrase and I think it's appropriate. Normansfield seemed to be separated from the outside world. When you stood outside the gates it did feel secluded even tho' it was next to a busy road. It was not very welcoming. There also wasn't much community involvement.*
>
> *Normansfield was quite an adventure for me. It was my first proper job and I was only nineteen years of age. Also leaving home and going abroad was quite a big step for me. My best friend persuaded me to come with her to England – just because she did not want to go alone and knew I would say yes. Indeed she was right. I have a lot of family in England so the choice was not difficult to make.*
>
> *When I went for the job interview I could not believe my eyes*

225

when I saw what was 'behind the wall'. A beautiful building appeared, which fascinates me to this day. I went to the reception office and saw beautiful mosaic tiles on the floor and a grand staircase with bright red carpet! You can imagine I was absolutely thrilled when I got the job. This story is of course only based on my personal views and experiences and can therefore differ from other people.

I was accepted as an assistant care staffer, grade A, at Cedar House. My contract hours were 37.5 per week. My roommate at Haydon House, who also worked at Cedar, was of great help throughout the first couple of weeks. Cedar House was based at the top floor. It was a long narrow corridor with high ceilings and squeaky floorboards. The men and women slept in separate corridors, the women near the theatre wing. Most shared a room. Three residents had their bedrooms on the first floor. The office was opposite the largest sitting room, and the kitchen was at the end of the corridor, which is now the Down's Syndrome Association office.

When I first started the job I had to get used to all the corridors of the main building and sometimes lost my sense of direction. There were several ways to get to Cedar. From Haydon House I normally used the front entrance by the car park (now the entrance to the Langdon Down Centre), but sometimes we used a shortcut via the fire escape until we were caught and reprimanded! For other facilities like the day centre, the residents took the stairs leading to the backyard. This also led to the reception office and the central kitchen. Those were the days with fresh cooked meals.

Cedar House was run by a manager and his deputy. When they were off duty, a qualified staff member was always in charge. The team was great and made me feel at home. In total we had about four staff on duty. At night two staff, one at each corridor. The night nursing officer would always pay a visit. I managed to survive three months of night duty, but had problems sleeping during the day, so I went back to day duty. Our am shift was 7.00 till 14.30 and the pm shift from 13.30 till 21.00. I think the night shift started at 20.30 till 7.00am. Our manager decided when we could have our breaks and sometimes let us off earlier if all the work was done. That was quite nice indeed! Because we would also do agency work when required, the team remained a stable factor for the residents.

The residents at Cedar had very different needs. Some were more independent; others needed extra help with their daily living skills, or had psychiatric needs and were not in the right place. Their communication skills varied. While some spoke few words, others were able to speak reasonable sentences. What I did notice while I was working at Cedar was that everything was done for them, so their skills were not encouraged or developed. I suppose the size of the group and the time factor was of influence, but on the other hand it may have become a work 'climate' that had never changed.

The interior of Cedar House was quite old and not very homely. The walls were covered with flowery wallpaper, which I thought was pretty old fashioned. No personal items could be found. Some of it had to do with a resident who threw a lot of stuff out the window, meaning all cupboards had to be locked. No money was spent on it for a long time. Two years later we moved to a bungalow, Oak House, which was an improvement. The furniture, decoration, and bedrooms were much nicer. Unfortunately some residents still had to share a bedroom.

At least it was not at bad as Willow and Elm, where they had to sleep in dormitories. These two bungalows were not suitable and should have been replaced years ago. Actually they were supposed to be temporary but were never rebuilt. After the inquiry, in 1979, Holly/Beach and Oak/Sycamore were built. Sycamore house had more residents with physical disabilities.

The facilities for these special needs could have been much better and more training on how to protect your back when carrying out physical work should have been given. There was a hoist available, but was used for one person only. The other bathroom was not adapted at all: a low bath and not even special shower facilities. I am also at fault for not asking advice. That was indeed not a great time for my back!

We worked on both sides because we became one team. Our daily tasks were very routine-based and individual needs were not always taken into consideration. There were set times for getting up and getting dressed, drinking tea or coffee, changing into their hospital pyjamas etc. With all the beds to make, I soon mastered the skill of folding corners! It was difficult to respect privacy because there were too many people sharing only two bathrooms.

Meal times were also quite hectic. At first I had to get used to the idea that we did not sit down for a meal together. I was told that the food was for the residents only. So we stood behind the counter and intervened when needed. I must say that the table manners were not brilliant. Nobody waited for each other and some would finish their pudding whilst walking to the counter. Few residents could not sit down together without poking someone with a fork or just pushing them away!

As a 'key worker' I was responsible for two residents. This meant I could spend extra time on individual needs by, for example, going for a walk, going shopping, having a drink at the residents' club, buying clothes and toiletries, or doing hair and make-up. Small things can make a big difference. There was a boutique on site but I preferred to buy clothes in Kingston. With one of 'my' residents it was possible to do activities outside the grounds, but the first appointment with the hairdresser was quite a challenge! I was pretty nervous myself, which of course did not help. With some residents of Normansfield that would have been extremely difficult and not really suitable. The key worker system was useful for me, although I do feel it very much depended on the attitude and abilities of the individual staff member.

During the week most residents went to the day centre, the Avenue centre, or a day centre outside Teddington (I believe in Staines). The day centre staff were an enthusiastic team and always organised the Christmas show at the theatre. One of our residents had quite difficult behaviour and could rip her clothes off at any time. A special programme was made for her. On a good day we took her to the hydrotherapy pool or the residents' club, which she enjoyed very much. Sometimes she ripped her clothes on your way back to the ward. I remember one incident when I took her back to Oak house. It must have looked quite silly with me running behind her trying to cover her up with a towel! Once a week, a disco was organised at the Avenue centre. At the weekends we often took them out for a drive in our minibus, for a walk, or to the residents' club for a cup of tea or coffee. The club was a great place for them. It was open every day.

Our yearly activities included 'Fun Day' (a barbecue and music), a boat trip to Hampton Court and the Christmas party at our theatre. The grounds created a lot of freedom and independence, as some residents went for a walk or to the facilities by themselves and enjoyed a chat with staff and residents. You would always meet someone on your way. I also enjoyed the contact with others. It was like a small community.

A lot of young people worked at Normansfield and several came from abroad. This made it an interesting place to work at. Also relationships were formed. I have good and bad memories of that period, but will cherish the time I fell in love for the first time (sadly the bloke in question did not know about it!).

Living at Haydon House was very cheap and also useful for getting in contact with other staff. Sometimes we went to the local pub, or organised activities. The social club was run by staff members but not many went there for a drink after work. It had to close down in the end. I don't know how long the Normansfield Football Club (for staff) existed, but several matches were organised and staff and residents came to watch. The football field was right at the back of Normansfield.

By the time I decided to leave the job and continue my nursing training in 1993, the decision had already been made to close Normansfield down. In order to guide this process a resettlement programme was introduced. Part of it was the Individual Programme Planning (IPP). In this care plan individuals' strengths/needs, likes/dislikes and goals were noted. I did find that very useful as it made you focus on the individual needs and work closer together with other professionals involved. All specialists worked on site (including the dentist), which was very practical. I did not have much contact with the management team and therefore cannot say much about their input.

I had mixed feelings about the whole resettlement process as for some residents Normansfield was a good place to be — had they improved all facilities. For others it would have been much better to participate in the local community. I remember one resident saying he would rather stay at Normansfield, as it had been his home for all his life. He enjoyed the freedom he had. It must have created a lot of stress. Sadly he died not long after.

I left Normansfield long before the move started, but have heard from my friend that it was a hectic period and felt staff morale had gone down. For the staff at Haydon House it was a very difficult time. They had to find a flat in the area and that was most *definitely too expensive. I do hope that all residents are happy in their new homes and do wonder what happened to the staff. I recently visited the only group who still live on site. They moved from the Kingston Road houses. It's now a lovely residential home where each resident has his or her own bedroom, toilet and washbasin. Also the manager is very much focused on the individual needs, but can understand that some changes will be difficult because of the life they had at Normansfield.*

Chapter eighteen

STOPPING THE CLOCKS & SILENCING THE PIANOS

Three members of the task force set up to help put the hospital back on its feet calmly continued their work. Terry Woods, Divisional Nursing officer of neighbouring Botley Park hospital is currently examining all nursing practices and procedures at Normansfield. With Dr Joan Bicknell and administrator, Colin Edwin, Mr Woods will advise the area management team on a day-to-day operational policy for Normansfield. The team has a wide remit to examine clinical nursing procedures, nursing care organisation, therapeutic services, social environment, maintenance of buildings and a host of other aspects of the running of the hospital. A community nursing service, based at Normansfield is to be set up. A short term care unit and day care unit also to be set up.

Nursing Mirror, 30 November 1978

Following the dramatic departure of Dr Terence Lawlor, the Kingston and Regional Health Authority created a task force to run the hospital and bring it into line with best practice elsewhere. One of the key figures appointed to it was Dr Joan Bicknell, who in 1980 had became the first ever Professor of Psychiatry in Learning Disability at St George's Hospital, south west London. Professor Bicknell was well aware of the appalling practices that had occurred at Normansfield in the 1970's. She described the standard of primary health care as absolutely disgraceful:

Simple illnesses were undiagnosed, immunisation not carried out.
Known medical complications of people with Down's syndrome
such as hearing, eyesight and hypothyroidism were left unchecked.

A number of patients at Normansfield with multiple disabilities were simply not given any special attention, despite being more likely to suffer from additional health problems. This is particularly surprising in light of how terrified Dr Lawlor was of anything going wrong. In response to these concerns, local GPs were brought in to provide primary health care.

Inevitably, staff morale was still low and Joan Bicknell remarked that:

There was a spirit of 'unhealthy' defiance from the old guard who
had supported Lawlor and thought that they had been doing some
things right.

The task force discovered that the residents' finances were also being mismanaged. A number of the patients who had remained in the hospital since nationalisation had private means, but they were not permitted access to their incomes for fear of staff stealing the money. Instead, the patients were given a tiny amount of pocket money each week called 'indigent monies' – a term which bewildered the professor.

However, the task force's most disturbing discovery was that of a punishment regime that Dr Lawlor had instigated. Following several instances of miscreant behaviour, a number of patients were forced to undergo freezing cold showers as a way of punishment and sometimes had their clothes taken away. John Langdon Down must have been spinning in his grave.

In order to improve nursing standards, nursing officer Terry Wood produced a 60 page booklet of guidelines for staff, *A Cause for Caring*. This addressed many of the difficulties that had arisen at the hospital in recent years and began with a mission statement:

Whatever the degree of handicap, the main aim of Normansfield is
to provide a pattern of living that is meaningful, suited to individual
needs, with the opportunity for the development of personality and
the preservation of human dignity.

In addition to this new care guidance, a team of social workers was appointed to liaise with families and interview every patient in the hospital. Their two main responsibilities during the first year were to update all the basic records so that the new psychiatrists would have a proper starting point from which to assess every patient thoroughly; and to formulate discharge plans for those residents who didn't need nursing care. After the task force disbanded, Professor Bicknell, remained at Normansfield as part-time Consultant Psychiatrist.

The *Sherrard Report* that followed the inquiry had criticised the state of the buildings and this led to a £1.3 million complex being proposed and built. The day centre and two bungalows (Oak and Willow), were added, providing more suitable accommodation for the physically handicapped and elderly residents.

In May 1981, *The Richmond and Twickenham Times* reported that, 'Normansfield is leading the way with its new approach to caring for the mentally handicapped.' This was an opinion apparently shared by the Parliamentary Under Secretary for Health, Sir George Young, who officially opened the new activity centre which catered for 115 people, 22 of them from outside the hospital. The new complex also included four new residential units each housing twelve people of mixed abilities. Young added:

> *I have been impressed by the improved quality of care the residents receive – much more human and much more of a homelike environment. We would desperately like to do more of this, not just in Normansfield but at other mental hospitals.*

The Avenue day centre, situated just outside the hospital grounds, was a community resource for the 'moderately mentally handicapped' and took users from special schools, the wider community or hospital. The main objective of the centre was:

> *To provide a system by which students abilities can be assessed, needs determined and met by programmed learning techniques until a point is reached when the total support of the centre can be withdrawn and the person can work and live unaided in the community.*

The centre offered some sheltered employment such as woodwork and metalwork workshops, pottery and horticulture. Prior to the centre opening, the hospital offered 'therapy units' where the residents were occupied by such tasks as painting, woodwork, basketry and repetitive, menial work like filling envelopes. Some of the patients worked in the grounds and a number of people were employed in the laundry. Others helped to deliver milk outside the hospital.

David Towell, whose sister, Pat, was a patient at Normansfield, recalls:

> There was a lot of energy in the task force and there was a nurse who was very active in trying to shake things up. I remember going to a relatives' meeting in the theatre, in about 1978. At the time it was proposed to open the bungalows and mix the sexes. Since they only had male and female wards, the new idea was that they be mixed. There was strong relative opposition to this and there was a big meeting – we ended up deciding it was a good idea after all. I think the phrase from Professor Bicknell was, 'Just because they are single sex wards doesn't mean there's no sex.' It was a thought which had never struck most of us.

Pat Towell was born in 1936 and soon after her birth contracted a severe case of whooping cough through which she suffered severe brain damage. Due to her developmental delay, she became extremely difficult to look after and this was exacerbated by the fact that Mrs Towell had to provide most of the care in war-torn London – the family was actually bombed out in 1941.

Pat was initially admitted to a local hospital, a few miles from the family home in Feltham. She was then moved further away to Royal Earlswood Hospital, in Redhill, Surrey, where her parents and David felt unable to visit so often:

> I remember going with our parents when I was about twelve to Royal Earlswood but being left in the car while they did the visiting. Clearly they found this painful and didn't want me to share their experience. Indeed I think they had stopped visiting altogether when I was a teenager – and it was not until more than thirty years later, after my father's death, that I was able to reintroduce Pat to our Mum.

Pat was later admitted to Normansfield. As he grew up, David decided he needed to know his sister better, although it was not until after he left university that he first met her again:

> *I think I sensed that Pat had become something of a 'closed chapter' in our parents' life and they might find it hard for me to re-open this book. I also wonder now whether, at least unconsciously, I was reluctant to let reality challenge the fantasy I had built up about my sister in the absence of information about her.*

David eventually visited her at Normansfield and was shown into an elegant lounge in the old building and, after a short wait, Pat was brought from her ward. He was immediately struck by the family resemblance: she shared their mother's wavy hair and their father's eyes and nose, but she also looked completely at odds with how he had imagined – 'the fantasy he had carried about with him for some time'.

David came to realise that Pat's home was not nearly as 'elegant' as first thought. The south wing housed about 50 women with varying capacities and all the women shared a single dormitory. During the day they spent most of their time 'milling around' one large room:

> *I can see now that as her brother, but also as part of our movement, I was able to play some part in shaping the second half of Pat's life for the better. Equally, and without ever "knowing" that she has a brother, Pat has profoundly shaped mine. Together, we still have much to do to advance the shared values we have gained through this experience.*

(Pat, now aged 70, lives the life of a dignified 'senior citizen' with two friends whom she has known for 30 years, in a purpose built group home a couple of miles from the house from which she was admitted to institutional care more than 60 years earlier.)

As 'our movement' suggests, David's interest was not just that of a concerned brother. He was also employed by an independent healthcare charity, the King's Fund, and his professional expertise was actually modernising older establishments, or 'the practice of achieving change in institutions'. David was, however, frustrated in

235

his vision to persuade the authorities to invest funds in genuine local community services, rather than building a new day centre and bungalows in the hospital grounds. These buildings were, in fact, knocked down after fewer than fifteen years when Normansfield closed.

Despite the injection of funds for new buildings and a day centre – overt political statements in light of the inquiry – financial restraints remained in place in other areas of the hospital. According to *The Surrey Comet* of December 1981:

> *Parents of patients at Normansfield Hospital are to start paying for nursing care for their children in the New Year to prevent loss of facilities because of spending cuts. The Friends of Normansfield has reluctantly decided to give Kingston and Richmond Area Health Authority £22,500 to pay for four extra nursing assistants at the hospital. This will help bring the staffing level near that recommended by the Task Force set up at the hospital after the Sherrard Inquiry Report. The hospital is at present understaffed and the authority has been unable to recruit because of overspending on the nursing budget by the Area Health Authority.*

Brian Rix, chairman of the League of Friends, was naturally dismayed that his organisation had been forced into funding health authority staff:

> *We understand that times are stringent and we understand there may have been a mess up in staffing, but we hope that this will prod the new district health authority into obtaining extra finance to see that the establishment figure can be quickly re-established.*

In fact, government policy was moving in the opposite direction, away from providing extra nursing staff for institutions such as Normansfield. *The Parkinson Report*, originally written in 1976 for the Conservative Party, was kept under wraps until 1981, two years after Margaret Thatcher was elected prime minister.

The report strongly endorsed community-based care and called for a determined programme of hospital closures, linked to a statutory duty and financial incentives for councils to make proper local provision. *Care in The Community* was the title of a Green

Paper that suggested ways of moving money and care from the National Health Service to local councils and voluntary associations:

> *Most people who need long-term care can and should be looked after in the community. That is what most of them want for themselves and what those responsible for their care believe to be best.*

Care in the Community applied especially to 'mentally handicapped', mentally ill and elderly patients. It suggested that 20,000 long-term patients (15,000 in mental handicap hospitals and 5,000 in mental illness hospitals) could be discharged 'immediately' if funds could be switched from the health service to local authorities.

One positive was that following the 1990 Community Care Act, the Department of Health officially adopted the less pejorative term 'people with learning difficulties'.

In the ensuing two decades, the meaning of community care evolved greatly but the direction was clear. Hospitalisation would no longer play a major role in the overall system of care. The plan was to provide services and care packages so that people could live in their home community. Patients did leave the hospitals but the practical assistance and finances were often insufficient, particularly in the hospital community care programme for the mentally ill. An edition of *The Epsom Guardian*, during this period, reported news that came as no surprise to those working at the local hospital:

> *It is generally accepted Normansfield will close, although no official date has been set. The Richmond, Twickenham and Roehampton District Health Authority, together with Richmond Council's social services department have drawn up a document recommending a programme of community support for people with learning difficulties. It is felt that Normansfield should play no long term role in future services as its continuing existence was acting as a disincentive for the development of community based services. The philosophy behind the proposal is that these groups of people should have the right to live in the community in ordinary housing. They will be encouraged to make choices and take decisions for themselves with social services managing their social care, and the health authority providing psychiatric care and other specialist support as well as general health care.*

In terms of Normansfield's closure, Kingston and Richmond Health Authority was slow off the mark. A National Development Team had visited in 1990, was highly critical, and called for a closure plan, which then took several years to formulate properly. A whole year was taken up in choosing and commissioning the appropriate housing associations to be involved in the break-up of the institution.

By 1993, Normansfield Hospital had become part of the new Richmond and Roehampton Healthcare NHS Trust. In September of that year there were still 96 patients in the old premises. Apart from the intention to move some of the residents to a highly structured 'halfway house' at 251 Kingston Road, new purpose built houses within the Normansfield grounds were due to take in others. One was a registered residential home; the others supported independent home living.

The consultation process with relatives was far from easy; some were very keen on closure and 'the quicker the better' and others were naturally more anxious about family members who may have spent their whole lifetime at Normansfield. They were in no hurry to agree to a precipitous and possibly inappropriate transfer.

There was inevitably some 'Nimby-ism' from nearby residents when locating some of the group homes and, depending on the relatives' viewpoint, either a great deal of careful planning and consultation in that period or, at worst, tokenistic discussion. According to some relatives, patients who had been friends for many years were separated and staff who knew the patients well, were not consulted about where they should be placed.

Normansfield, working with the Mencap Homes Foundation (in which Elspet Rix was playing a key local role), had made a start on moving more able residents into community settings. Elspet considered that there was sufficient consultation about patients moving out, although she felt that the needs of the patients were often greater than the support provided, despite the intentions of the Community Care Act. The Rix's daughter, Shelley, was transferred to a Mencap group home in 1990.

David Towell, who was by now Chair of the Normansfield Parents, Relatives and Advocates Association, believed that, overall, the closure was managed well and much attention was given to individual needs. His sister, Pat, moved to her new home in 1997 with a very detailed care plan, including physiotherapy and occupational therapy, a summary of her situation and an outline of how her needs might change. David also commented that it was the first time Pat had her own bedroom since she was a child.

A key figure in the break-up of Normansfield was psychologist Wolf Wolfensberger, already a significant figure in the world of learning disability. He had first been inspired to work for better rights for disabled people in the mid-1950's when he was employed and outraged by the conditions in the wards of a mental institution in Nebraska. His work on 'Normalization' and citizen advocacy in the late 1960's and early 1970's has been acknowledged as major influences on working with learning disabled people.

Wolfensberger's 1983 theory of the 'Social Role, Valorization' (SRV) was the model used in the closure plans for Normansfield and because of his expert knowledge of John Langdon Down, Wolfensberger was actually invited to lecture at the hospital.

To explain SRV in this setting is not easy; whole books have been written on the subject. It has been defined as 'a service theory based on empirical knowledge for the delivery of services to people with any kind of need or condition, but especially those who are devalued' . . . in other words, an approach to care which views people as individuals of worth and plans for them with respect and without prejudice.

Wolfensberger was also extremely keen on the provision of appropriate support on an individual basis and believed 'the protection and advancement of human rights and dignity' was paramount. Wolfensberger, who believed that people in institutional care needed independent representation by people in their communities if they were ever going to experience normal living, also coined the term 'Citizen Advocacy'. The appointment of advocates is one way in which people who are in any way disadvantaged or vulnerable can be supported and encouraged to strive for their basic rights and needs as a citizen.

The advocate's tasks is to represent the views and interests of someone who has been discriminated against as if they were their own, and offer understanding and practical support – basically to ensure their 'partner' receives everything to which he or she is entitled. The Normansfield Parents Association were very keen on the involvement of such advocates although the manager of

Normansfield at the time, Arthur Morgan, like Terence Lawlor before him, was anxious that the association would not give relatives the chance to voice grievances.

One such advocate was Denise Carr, who acted for Carol Miller (1943-2005), a patient at Normansfield for nearly 30 years. Through her role, Denise also became a member of the League Of Friends. Denise was much influenced by and found herself in agreement with Wolfensberger's ideals, feeling that people with learning difficulties needed objective support other than the care they received from paid professional workers. Denise's father suffered from multiple sclerosis and it was during his hospitalisation and residency at a nursing home that Denise, then only a small child, first became involved in the practice of how institutions can affect an individual's life. In the mid 1980's, while working for the Bank of England, she seized her chance to become involved:

*Carol Miller.
Diagnosed as a
'mental defective'
at the age of
seven in 1950
and subsequently
a Normansfield
resident for nearly
30 years.*

I saw an article about Citizen Advocacy in one of the local free papers and I think it appealed to me because of the advocacy side of it, as much as the befriending side. I felt that was something I could do, and I liked the idea of the one to one relationship rather than just going along as a volunteer and helping generally.

Denise quite rightly feels that parents or relatives often have to hold back about complaints or criticism of staff or the institution because they fear that there will be some backlash against their relative. In contrast, she says:

An advocate provides an objective voice speaking up on behalf of the patient. Also some patients don't have any family to support them and are isolated.

Denise initially approached an organisation called 'Citizen Advocacy' and then visited Normansfield. The staff were caring but understaffed, undervalued and institutionalised and she was horrified by some of the levels of disability she discovered at the hospital:

It was awful. I was staggered at the degree of handicap – the physical handicap, erratic behaviour. I thought, 'Oh God, this is not for me!' So I came away quite convinced then that I couldn't become an advocate after all.

When she was told that there was a young woman who was moving out of Normansfield and who needed an advocate urgently, Denise was, however, persuaded otherwise. Carol Miller was at that time a resident of Cedar House which, according to Denise, was awful:

All the residents used to sit around in wheelchairs or armchairs, half asleep. It was really depressing. There were all those beautiful grounds but none of patients could enjoy them. So we used to go out and around the grounds or visit the local park. Sometimes we used to come back to my house and have tea.

Carol had endured a difficult childhood. She was born with a cleft palate and underwent corrective surgery at the age of five. In 1950, when she was seven years old, a doctor examined her and ascertained her to be 'a mental defective'. It was recorded that she may have suffered from lead poisoning as a child. The following year she started visiting an occupational centre (later known as Hillingdon Training School).

Carol could wash and dress but couldn't read. She could only write her name. She was eventually admitted to Normansfield in 1957 at the age of fourteen. Her mother died when she was quite young and her father (now also deceased) last visited his daughter in 1975. There was no contact from any other relatives.

Carol suffered from the coordination disorder, dyspraxia, which caused communication problems and she was incontinent of urine at night. She slept in an open ward and she had absolutely no privacy from the other women patients. According to Denise, Carol's own clothing all seemed to have been lost and her possessions, such as they were, remained in a wardrobe by her bed. Carol was not provided with the sufficient care and support she needed and there was a lot of work for Denise in her early days of advocacy. She attempted to get something done about Carol's severe speech and weight problems and also tackled Carol's difficulties in hygiene. No physical or psychological reason had ever been discovered for Carol's nocturnal enuresis, although whenever she went on holiday and only shared a room with one member of staff instead of occupying a ward, she was not incontinent.

Carol had some assistance and support in cooking and road safety, but it was always going to be difficult for her to live independently. She had worked in a café and had a couple of other part time jobs, but had never received a working wage. Carol was very friendly and thus popular with staff and other patients. She attended various clubs, liked going to the cinema, galleries and bowling and enjoyed needlework and music and movement classes.

With Denise's prompting, it was decided that Carol should be one of the first patients to move to a halfway house where she would receive support from care staff. Unfortunately, her transfer was delayed for months because of a shortage of staff, refitting of the accommodation and even a lack of furniture. Eventually, in February 1986, Carol moved into 251 Kingston Road, which she shared with Gordon Bairnsfather and a young man, David, with whom she had a very good friendship. David could explain Carol's needs when she couldn't make herself understood. They were pretty inseparable and used to go on bus rides together, also enjoying regular trips to Heathrow.

The semi-independence of Kingston Road gave Carol much more confidence. Her speech improved and she learned some Makaton sign language, although she was, of course, dependent on other people knowing and using it in her presence.

Apart from acting as her advocate in terms of practical support, Denise visited Carol every Sunday for 25 years, taking her on visits, walks and sharing gardening and shopping outings. Denise even used to take her to see her own mother in Kilburn regularly. Denise felt that Carol, who for the majority of her adult life had no input from relatives, was robbed of ordinary family pursuits which the nursing staff just weren't able to emulate:

> *The residents did have social activities but due to lack of staff, they had to go out in groups with other disabled people. It was much easier for me to provide individual attention than a member of staff who just didn't have the time and had many other responsibilities.*

With assistance, Carol managed to live at Kingston Road for nearly 20 years but when frailty required her to move into the Langdon Park residential home in March 2004. Sadly, within a few months she had a stroke and was hospitalised for nine months before she died. A memorial seat was purchased for Carol and placed in the residential home grounds.

According to Denise, Carol never talked about her early life or her parents. In common with a great many fellow patients, 'Normansfield was her life'.

The distinguished sociologist, Erving Goffman, wrote *Asylums*, a series of essays about institutional inmates in 1961. He describes how the staff, who are themselves institutionalised and ruled by rigid hierarchy, have to run the organisation as smoothly as possible, even at the expense of the patients. The hospital routine became paramount. He defines 'total institutions' and explains the numerous ways in which the individual patient is stripped of all his or her character and has no option but to conform. No era throughout the history of Normansfield has witnessed the results of institutionalisation more than during the Terence Lawlor administration, when patients were treated with contempt and robbed of any self respect. There is no doubt that even the most dedicated and decent members of staff are likely to be defeated by the system.

As David Appleman states in his excellent article, *Living In The Margin*, the men, women and children whose lives were moulded by their physical or learning disabilities and spent their whole lives in institutions were further stigmatised, 'During the early 1980's, it was clear that the institutional regime was failing patients terribly. As the decade drew to a close, the system had progressively deteriorated to the verge of near collapse.'

Closure of such institutions was inevitable; in 2001, the Government published a White Paper called *Valuing People*. The document stated that it would help people with learning disabilities 'to live full and independent lives as part of their local communities.' David Towell, who now works as an advocate for both 'Inclusion Europe and Inclusion International' is of the opinion that closing all the institutions was no more than a first step in advancing the agenda for a more inclusive society and one that values 'all its members'. According to David, *Valuing People* put 'learning disability' firmly on the public agenda, producing a radical policy framework for 21st century progress.

CHAPTER NINETEEN

THE SPIRIT LIVES ON

The hours of a wise man are lengthened by his ideas.

Joseph Addison, poet and essayist (1672-1719)

In February 1999, the first public meeting was held to discuss plans for a housing development on the site of Normansfield Hospital. Property developers, Laing Homes, submitted two planning applications for the site, which included proposals to build more than 150 homes and the possibility of converting the hospital building itself into a hotel. After much bureaucratic negotiation, the site was sold to Laing homes for an undisclosed amount and agreement reached on the construction of 198 houses and apartments on the 32 acre site. Ten acres were developed and the remainder, excluding the listed building were left as green space. As part of the Section 106 planning agreement, Laing Homes spent £1.5 million on refurbishing the hospital building, and the theatre and its historic listed scenery.

When the work was completed in 2004, the freehold of the old entertainment hall and adjacent offices were sold to the Langdon Down Charity Trust for the princely sum of one pound. The Trust had been formed by people with an interest in Normansfield. Its patron is Lord Rix and trustees include Elspet Rix, Carol Boys, Chief Executive of the Down's Syndrome Association and Professor Conor Ward.

The Down's Syndrome Association now rents office space on the top two floors of the theatre wing but the story of how the organisation returned to their 'spiritual home' is one of extraordinary coincidence. Carol Boys describes the events:

In 2003 I discovered quite by chance that my husband Paul, who was then employed by Laing Homes, was involved in the purchase of the old hospital and surrounding land for a housing development. He had no idea about the significance of the place and I had never visited Normansfield and I don't think I would have thought about going there had it not been for a phone call from Professor Ward who was researching the work of John Langdon Down.

Professor Ward was concerned that Normansfield had been bought by a developer and that the old entertainment hall was going to be turned into a theatre museum. He had rescued a substantial archive of material from the building including many photographs and papers dating from the late 1800's. He was of the opinion that the archive should be displayed and the building, including the theatre, should be used for people with learning disabilities – as it was always intended.

Carol was understandably amazed and decided at that stage to keep quiet about the fact that she had any connection with the developer until she had found out more information:

I was taken aback by this phone call, and listened as Professor Ward said that he wanted me to support him to persuade the developer to include the Down's Syndrome Association in the consultation about the Theatre.

Carol and husband Paul duly visited the site together and although most of the main building was derelict, the theatre seemed to have miraculously escaped any damage. Carol took one look at the buildings and following the discovery of Walter Ridpath's remarkable effects (see chapter 4) felt that this fortuitous connection was more than just a mere coincidence: it was somehow 'meant to be'. Carol decided that the Down's Syndrome Association must now be involved in the future of Normansfield:

We had a responsibility to make sure that the wonderful archive material was preserved and made available to the public.

The Down's Syndrome Association took up residency in 2004 and now share the premises with a number of other groups. Twenty

The ebullient Down 2 Earth group.

One and Co are a local group who hold arts and speech and language sessions twice a week for children with Down's syndrome and Dragon Drama run regular workshops for local children. Concerts and conferences also take place in the theatre.

Another important gathering who meet monthly in the Normansfield Theatre is the Down 2 Earth Group. It was set up by the Down's Syndrome Association information team in 2002 as a focus group where young adults could discuss subjects of mutual interest and importance to them, as well as share common experiences of living with Down's syndrome. Down 2 Earth has a core membership of 25 people with wide ranging abilities and communication skills – but all with very much to say. The first work that the group undertook with the information team was to help write an accessible health booklet and a welcome pack to encourage adults with Down's syndrome to join the DSA.

Since then the group has covered a wide range of subjects: how to find a job, how to be assertive and increase self-confidence; and how to form romantic and sexual relationships – a topic, according to information officer Susannah Seyman, that is a very popular theme and often re-visited.

Down 2 Earth have also branched out. Last spring they travelled to Belfast to represent England in the Five Nations Conference Weekend. The group have all grown together and supported each other in the last few years in life-changing events such as leaving home, leaving college, seeking employment and inevitably . . . falling in love!

Susannah Seyman, whose introduction to Normansfield is described in the preface to this book, is encouraged by the changes she has seen:

> It so heartening to see and be part of this lively, feisty group who come to this building, not to be oppressed – you just try oppressing them! – hidden away and ignored, but to voice their opinions and be listened to, and generously and invaluably to inform the work of the Down's Syndrome Association and other groups and researchers who have been in contact with them.

The group publish a regular magazine, edited by one of its members, the dazzling Kate Powell, and has contributions such as letters, drawings, poems and recipes solely contributed by adults with Down's syndrome.

One of the group's most recent tasks was to advise the production staff of BBC soap opera *EastEnders* in a storyline that

Kate Powell, editor of the Down 2 Earth magazine.

involves a baby with Down's syndrome. It is wholly appropriate that the views of people with Down's syndrome should be sought and listened to in the making of the programme and the group's contribution to the soap was acknowledged by story editor, Jane Perry, with a visit for Down 2 Earth to the *EastEnders* set at Elstree Studios in autumn 2006.

The 'thank you' visit was a huge success and one of the group was so overcome at meeting some of Albert Square's most famous characters that he told everyone, 'I've just been to the land of my dreams'.

This is all a long way away from the bigoted descriptions by Dr Tredgold in the 1920's:

> *Some of these are mild, placid, inoffensive creatures who give little trouble . . . the excitable type on the other hand are passionate, violent, untrustworthy and intractable. They will destroy clothes, toys, picture books and if left alone for a few hours, the probability is that they will either wreck the room or set fire to it.*

And yet learning disabled people continue to be excluded from many areas of society and it remains a struggle to gain independence and basic rights. Disturbing stories are still not uncommon – I heard of a London based GP who as recently as 2005 couldn't bring himself to utter the words Down's syndrome, confirming the diagnosis to a distraught mother by saying:

> *Yes, the baby has forty-seven chromosomes, but don't worry: they don't live longer than forty-five years of age.*

That said (patently untrue) he ushered the woman out of the door.

As I write, a news story is breaking: an investigation by the Healthcare Commission into conditions and care at the Orchard Hill hospital in Carshalton run by the Sutton and Merton primary care trust discovered that people with learning disabilities had been subjected to continuing physical and sexual abuse. Patients at the hospital and at other units run by the trust had been 'treated in outdated and infantilising ways' and that 'living conditions were impoverished'.

As a result the commission is launching a nationwide audit

and inspection of learning disability services. It is likely that responsibility for such services will pass from the NHS to local councils.

In addition, the Royal College of Obstetricians & Gynaecologists, an institution pledged to the advancement of science, is calling for an open debate about the ethics of euthanasia for the 'sickest' of newborn children. The College is providing evidence to the Nuffield Council on Bioethics and suggest that we should think more radically about non-resuscitation, withdrawal of treatment decisions and active euthanasia as a means of widening 'the management options'. The Nuffield inquiry is looking at:

> . . . the ethics of prolonging life in foetuses and the newborn and the inherent enormous social, emotional and financial costs.

I think we can guess which way this is going . . .

Although Normansfield officially closed as an institution in 1999, there is one 'resident' who evidently still occupies the hospital to this day.

First spotted by nursing staff in the 1950's, a ghost has been witnessed on a number of occasions since the arrival of the Down's Syndrome Association. Sightings and experiences have been quite common and although many have remained sceptical, there does seem to be an awful lot of evidence.

Several members of staff at the Langdon Down Centre have heard unexplained footsteps when the building has been empty, for example. And a pest controller, called in to exterminate a number of pigeons that had flown in through a hole in the theatre roof, was scared out of his wits by mysterious sounds and left the building hurriedly, refusing ever to return. An electrician coming into lay some cables felt a tap on his shoulder but when he turned around there was no one there . . .

One of the conservators of the theatre scenery, who had not heard any of the stories about the ghost, heard footsteps and glimpsed a small man in top hat and frock coat. Rosalind Georgeson from the Dragon Drama theatre group had a similar encounter:

I was there one early evening in the winter of 2005. The whole building was empty apart from us and it was dark outside. I left the theatre by the side door and I observed a dark figure at the top of the stairs to my left. The figure moved very quickly up the next flight of stairs, as if I had 'caught' them unawares and they didn't want to be seen. My first reaction was that a member of staff must be working late. But then I realised that being early evening, the office workers had all gone home!

The Langdon Down Trust's Sandra Maltby adds to the mystery.

I was in the lift on the first floor and the doors kept opening and closing. They did this five or six times before finally closing. Carol Boys and I have both been in the basement discussing an exhibition when photographs have suddenly fallen off the wall and a window has flown open. Yet the windows down there are very stiff and take a bit of effort to open.

Peter Longman, patron of the Theatres Trust, says:

I never saw a ghost but I always feel I have to speak to the theatre when I go in there so that it knows I am a 'friend'. A piece of glass from the lighting batten once fell at my feet and smashed for no reason, and the "act drop" dropped and split when we talked about taking it down for repairs. There is definitely something strange about the place!

There are, of course, varying theories on the ghost's identity: one supposition is that it is the spectre of Everleigh Langdon Down, killed by brother Reginald in the carpenter's shop in 1883. This is based on the fact that he always appears at the same time – either at 5.30 or 6.30 in the evening (depending on whether it is GMT or BST) and this is almost exactly the time that Everleigh died from his wounds.

Some people who have witnessed some paranormal activity have described the presence as unthreatening . . . almost friendly. He is apparently of diminutive height and so some are convinced that this gentle being is a man with Down's syndrome. Reports of

'Girl with Hoop'.
This exquisite bronze statue
by sculptor, Andre Wallace,
glistens in the old orchard of
the Normansfield grounds
and portrays a figure
confronting life's challenge
with confidence and hope.

formal Edwardian attire lend themselves to the assertion that the spirit is Walter Ridpath, whose personal effects so mysteriously came to light during Carol Boys' initial visit to Normansfield in 2003.

However, no one would be surprised if this was an apposite reincarnation of the great man himself, John Langdon Down, whose spiritual embodiment maintains a living presence at Normansfield in the form of the Down's Syndrome Association, simply keeping an eye on events unfolding in his old home.

Forever associated with the eponymous syndrome – the single most common cause of learning difficulties – John Langdon Down's work extended to other disabilities and throughout his distinguished career, he exhibited genuine concern, a pioneering approach and a true motivation to ameliorate the lives of the learning disabled. He was indeed a long way ahead of his time and the first to recognise the potential of men, women and children who had been discarded by everyone else.

He transformed the lives of so many people with learning disabilities and set a standard and moral example which even after all these years has seldom been equalled.

Francesca Byrne sums up John Langdon Down's timely contribution perfectly:

> *The Victorian obsession with propriety and social order often led to the demonisation and ostracism of those most in need of inclusion and care. John Langdon Down was among the first to spearhead the campaign for what was to become a more widespread acceptance of those with learning disabilities. His classification of Down's syndrome, coupled with innovative beliefs on the training and education of his patients, established him as someone who tirelessly strove to remove the chains of the afflicted.*

It is wholly fitting that site of the old Normansfield hospital is now vibrant with innovative endeavour and is a testament to the energy, inspiration and spirit of the Langdon Down family. According to Carol Boys:

> *There is a truly inclusive atmosphere at Normansfield. It buzzes with activity. John Langdon Down would have certainly approved.*

BIBLIOGRAPHY

JOHN LANGDON DOWN, A CARING PIONEER

Professor O Conor Ward
The Royal Society of Medicine Press Ltd 1998

DR LANGDON DOWN AND THE NORMANSFIELD THEATRE

A thesis for MPhil in modern and Contemporary British and Irish Drama
Jessica Byrne
2004

THE NORMANSFIELD PROJECT

Heather Cadbury

TESTIMONIES OF RESISTANCE, EXPLORING EXPERIENCES OF ADVOCACY BY PEOPLE WITH LEARNING DISABILITIES

Heather Cadbury
Edited by Duncan Mitchell
Published by Jessica Kingsley 2006

FORGOTTEN LIVES: EXPLORING THE HISTORY OF LEARNING DISABILITY

Dorothy Akinson, Mark Jackson and Jan Walmsley
BILD publications 2003

MENTAL DISABILITY IN VICTORIAN ENGLAND THE EARLSWOOD ASYLUM 1847 – 1901

David Wright
The Clarendon Press 2001

MENTAL DEFICIENCY

A. F Treadgold
William wood and Co 1911

OUT OF SIGHT

Steve Humphries and Pamela Gordon
Channel 4 publishing 1992

THE POLITICS OF MENTAL HANDICAP

Joanna Ryan with Frank Thomas
Free Association Books Re-issued 1987

MENTAL AFFECTIONS OF CHILDHOOD AND YOUTH

John Langdon Down
Mac Keith Press 1990

THE MONGOL IN OUR MIDST

F.G. Crookshank
Kegan Paul, Trench Trubner and Co 1925

REPORT OF THE COMMITTEE OF INQUIRY INTO NORMANSFIELD HOSPITAL

HMSO 1978 Cmnd. 7357

A MINOR ADJUSTMENT

Andy Merriman
Macmillan 1999

ASYLUMS

E. Goffman
Penguin 1961

THE HISTORY OF TAMESIS CLUB

Berry Ritchie published by Tamesis Club May 2002

MY FARCE FROM MY ELBOW

Brian Rix
Secker and Warburg 1975

FARCE ABOUT FACE

Brian Rix
Hodder and Stoughton   1989

LIVING IN THE MARGIN

David Appleman
Article in Variant Magazine (Winter 1999/2000)

THE AUTHOR

Andy Merriman lives in north London with his wife, Alison and their three children, Daniel, Sarah and Joel.

Andy has written comedy sketches for television, several comedy drama series and plays for BBC radio and has contributed many articles to various magazines, newspapers and websites. Andy has also written three plays for the Association of Scientific Education – used for teaching purposes in the National Curriculum Citizenship Syllabus.

Tales of Normansfield is his sixth book and he is currently writing the authorised biography of actress Hattie Jacques. Andy is a keen follower of Sergeant Bilko, Bill Evans and Tottenham Hotspur – although not necessarily in that order . . .

Andy with daughter Sarah, his muse.